My Right Hand in the Father's

Knowing God's Comfort and Strength through Breast Cancer

By
Helen E Jones

First Published in 2012
Copyright © Helen E Jones

First published by Verité for
Helen E Jones

Printed by Verité CM Limited,
124 Sea Place, Goring by Sea, West Sussex
BN12 4BG UK

ISBN No: 978-1-907636-53-0

Cover image kindly donated by dennisanthony, lifestyle photographer -
www.dennisanthony.co.uk 'take my hand' © dennisanthony 2012

DEDICATION

In loving memory of my dear friend,
Jill Pennington
26.9.65 - 29.7.09.

An amazingly faithful lady
and inspiration to all breast
cancer sufferers.

Thank You!

Thank you to my husband, Ian, who has not only read and edited this book, and corrected all my grammatical mistakes, but who has stood by me, supported me and loved me throughout it all. You are my absolute soul mate and my best friend and I will love you forever! Thank you to my boys, Ben and Oli, for loving me when I was bald, fat and grumpy, and for getting me through the worst time of my life. You are my life's inspiration and I will always love you. Thank you to my dad and my sisters, Jan and Louise - I will never forget your incredible care, love and kindness throughout this time and throughout my life. I love you all so very much.

To all the other family members, dear friends, work colleagues and church family at St Mark's, Haydock - thank you for all your prayers, encouragement and practical help. Your love, faithfulness and friendship kept me going. Thank you to all my new friends at Trinity Theological College and at St Matthew's, Bristol. Your prayers and encouragement inspire me to work towards seeing my vision of a Christian cancer ministry start in the UK. Thank you to Rachel for taking the time to proof read and edit this book, and to Ro for getting me started with 'Firm Roots Cancer Support' and helping me to see that all things are possible with the Lord God. Lastly, thank you to Verité for agreeing to publish my story.

May God richly bless you all.

Table Of Contents

Introduction

For years I've thought about writing a book, often reading novels and thinking I could write one equally as good. Never in a million years did I imagine that I would write a book about my experience of breast cancer, because like so many women, I never imagined it could happen to me.

As I am travelling through this journey, I am so grateful to God for the comfort and strength he gives me every day, and I don't know how I would cope without his constant presence and encouragement. He feels like my personal trainer - the ultimate one who directs me and keeps me going through every stage of this process. I am also so blessed because of my family - my precious husband Ian, my beautiful boys Ben and Oliver, my wonderful dad and sisters, Jan and Louise. There are so many other family members and friends who have all shown me amazing, and often deeply humbling, love and support - often reaching out to me like the very practical hands and loving arms of God himself.

My purpose in writing this book is to share with other women the very real comfort and peace God has given me during my diagnosis and treatment. This book documents my experiences, my thoughts and emotions, but also my prayers, Bible verses, words and encouragements that God and other people have given me. I hope there will also be a few chuckles along the way! If you are a lady whose life has been turned upside down because of breast cancer, or any other cancer, then I hope that by sharing my story, you too may find hope, peace, strength and comfort from your heavenly father. In the Bible, Peter said that 'God… is not far from each one of us' (Acts 17 v 27) and I pray that on the journey through your illness, you too would know him holding your right hand.

With much love in Christ,

Helen Jones

"And the God of all grace, who called you to his eternal glory in Christ,
after you have suffered a little while, will himself restore you and
make you strong, firm and steadfast."
1 Peter 5 v 10

"But now, this is what the Lord says -
he who created you, O Jacob,
he who formed you, O Israel:
'Fear not, for I have redeemed you;
I have summoned you by name;
you are mine.
When you pass through the waters,
I will be with you;
And when you pass through the rivers, they will not sweep over you.
When you walk through the fire, you will not be burned;
The flames will not set you ablaze.
For I am the Lord your God......
Since you are precious and honoured in my sight,
and because I love you."
Isaiah 43 v 1-4

'I keep my eyes always on the LORD.
With him at my right hand, I will not be shaken.'
Psalm 16 v 8

Chapter One
Turning 40

On 22nd February 2010, I celebrated my 40th birthday. I had some trepidation about entering my 40s, but it didn't seem such a big leap as turning 30 had done, a decade before - after which I remember feeling very old and rather miserable! However, when my 40th birthday eventually arrived, it was absolutely brilliant. I had so many celebrations - a girls' dinner dance night out, a spa weekend with my husband, a big family meal and other meals with friends. In fact my brother-in-law complained that it was the longest and most celebrated 40th birthday ever and he was glad when it was all over! I laughed so much and so heartily during those three weeks - yes the celebrations did span over a three week period! On the girls' party night, everybody wore 'head boppers' with a picture of me looking like Shrek. I was dressed in an 'outfit' my sister made for the same occasion - a black nightdress with lots of red '40s' everywhere. When my friend's daughter saw a photo of me, she asked "Why did Auntie Helen dress up as a ladybird?" I remember coming home from the spa weekend away, only to find enormous photos of me, again looking like Shrek - in the ladybird outfit and worse - all over my estate as 'speeding 40 signs.' These were stuck on all of the lampposts and there was an enormous one planted in my front garden for everyone to see! All very embarrassing, but very funny to look back at!

I remember during the spa weekend, my husband Ian went off for some quality time at a local pub to watch his beloved Manchester United, and left me to shrivel up in the jacuzzi. I had such an overwhelming feeling of my life being utterly blessed. When I thought about all the many blessings and wonderful things God had given to me, it brought me to tears. I just lay there amid the bubbles, thanking him for my lovely husband, my two precious boys, Ben and Oliver, and for my wider family: my dad, my lovely mum (who had died eight years before), my sisters - who are also my best friends - and my brother, aunties and uncles. I also gave thanks for my friends, my church, my work, the children that I work with, my health, my house, my car, deaf friends and my love of signing. The list seemed to go on and on and on. As I prayed in that place, I just had a tiny, miniscule sense of foreboding, as if something was going to happen to shake all of this. I immediately prayed for protection for my dad, nan and father-in-law, hoping nothing was going to happen to any of them. The feeling soon passed and I basked again in the joy of being loved by God and utterly blessed by him.

> *Thank you Lord that you know me and love me completely.*
> *I feel so surrounded by your love and I thank you with all my heart, for the abundant blessings you have poured into my life and the many gifts you have given me.*
> *Thank you for creating me and for my 40 years of life!*
> *Thank you for making me yours and for filling me with joy and peace.*

Help me to live the rest of my life in service to you - honouring and blessing you Lord, just as you have blessed me.

Amen

'For you created my inmost being;
you knit me together in my mother's womb.
I praise you because I am fearfully and wonderfully made;
Your works are wonderful,
I know that full well.
My frame was not hidden from you when I was formed
    in that secret place.
When I was woven together in the depths of the earth,
Your eyes saw my unformed body.
All the days ordained for me were written in your book before
    one of them came to be.'
Psalm 139 v 13-16

Chapter Two
The Beginning

When my 40th birthday celebrations finally ended, it was time for the serious issue of getting fit and looking after my body. As a busy working mum with a sweet tooth and a love of chocolate, I had never managed to lose the weight I had gained from having my children, the youngest of whom had been born a whole nine years earlier. Oh dear. It was time to eat more healthily, attack the cellulite and get fit, not fat, at forty!

I had known a couple of friends and colleagues who had had breast cancer in their forties and so I decided that as part of this new healthy, 'looking after your body because you're getting older' mentality, I needed to start checking my breasts. This is something I had hardly ever done and when I had, it was a general 'feel' and I had never really known how exactly to check and also at what time of the month. I'm sure other ladies will agree that breasts often seem naturally lumpy and tender at different points during the monthly cycle, so it was just a bit too tricky.

I'll never forget the first time I did a 'proper', thorough check, because right at the back of my right breast, I found a hard lump I had never felt before. I immediately dismissed it and walked out of the bathroom, but a strong and sudden wave of worry washed over me and I started to tremble. I returned to the bathroom and checked again. It was still there... in the same place... a definite 'lump.' I just stood for a moment - my face completely drained of colour, heart pounding, hands shaking. Surely not. Surely God wouldn't allow anything like that to happen to me?

For a brief moment I thought about not telling my husband Ian, and just pretending I hadn't noticed it. But then I remembered my mum. My precious mum died of endometrial cancer at only 56 years of age because it had been undiagnosed. I had sworn after that, that I would always go to the doctor and request tests if ever I had any concerns. And so I decided, because of my mum and for the sake of my children, I had to be bold and face up to it, tell my husband and go to my doctor straight away.

Ian knew immediately that there was something wrong and as I told him, I burst into tears. He was upset for me, but stayed calm and tried to reassure me that it was probably nothing. I couldn't face going to church that morning so Ian took the boys and I stayed at home, crying, worrying and praying. As I prayed, I remembered one of my favourite verses in the Bible from Jeremiah 29 v 11.

'For I know the plans I have for you. Plans to prosper you and not to harm you. Plans to give you hope and a future.'

I felt reassured that my life was completely in God's hands and tried to muster up the strength to believe that nothing bad could happen to me, but still fears and worry flooded in. In my heart I knew that God did allow bad things to happen to his people, but that he promised to be with them through the trials.

Lord I feel afraid and sick and scared.
I'm worried about tomorrow and about the future.
I'm worried about doctors and hospitals; tests and procedures.
Help me to lay my worries at your feet
and not to keep hold of them.
Help me to remember my life is totally in your hands.
I am your child and you are my father.
Whatever the future holds, I know you will be with me
and I ask that you will give me strength.
Amen

The next morning I got an emergency appointment with my GP, who confirmed that there was a lump but said to me it was 'probably nothing serious' and I could return in a couple of weeks for her to check again. She gave me the option of being referred to the consultant immediately or in another couple of weeks. I couldn't bear the thought of waiting and worrying for another few weeks, and delaying the investigation process further, so I asked to be referred straight away for my own peace of mind.

Whilst I was there, I asked my doctor about when and how to check breasts and she said women should check themselves every month, immediately after their period. At the back of this book is further information on how to check your breasts. I am determined, in view of my story, to somehow raise women's awareness and increase education about breast-checking, because so many of my friends have said that they, like me, rarely or never check themselves. Breast cancer can affect anyone at any age, not just the over 50s who are regularly screened in the UK.

Looking back now, I praise God that I found that lump then. As I realised later, had I not discovered it when I did, I could have been in serious trouble.

A TIME FOR EVERYTHING

'There is a time for everything,
and a season for every activity under heaven:
a time to be born and a time to die,
a time to plant and a time to uproot,
a time to kill and a time to heal,
a time to tear down and a time to build,
a time to weep and a time to laugh,
a time to mourn and a time to dance,
a time to scatter stones and a time to gather them up,
a time to embrace and a time to refrain,
a time to search and a time to give up,
a time to keep and a time to throw away,
a time to tear and a time to mend,
a time to be silent and a time to speak,
a time to love and a time to hate,
a time for war and a time for peace.
… He has made everything beautiful in its time.'
Ecclesiastes 3 v 1-8, v 11.

Chapter Three
Testing and Waiting

Within only a few days of my GP appointment, I received two letters to say I had been given an appointment with the breast consultant the following Tuesday, and only eight days after visiting my doctor. I was really impressed by how quickly I was given an appointment, and to this day I am incredibly grateful to the NHS, and to all the staff in Wigan who cared for me, for their excellent standard of care and speed of service. My main concern was that Ian was going to America on a business trip the Saturday before my appointment and he would be away for two weeks. This felt like terrible timing and part of me was dreading going through the tests without him. One of my sisters was away on holiday and the other was at work.

In the days preceding my appointment, I tried to stay calm and not worry and kept trying to push it all to the back of my mind. However, I inevitably felt anxious and tense at times, and often found myself shouting at the boys or crying for no apparent reason.

It's hard to trust God in the waiting times. When we don't see an answer or know what is going to happen, it's easy to be afraid. But I think that while we are waiting, in the darkness of uncertainty - that is when we need him most and when he can do a powerful work of strength in us.

> *'The Lord is my light and my salvation - whom shall I fear?*
> *The Lord is the stronghold of my life - of whom shall I be afraid?'*
> *Psalm 27 v 1-2*

> *'I lift up my eyes to the hills - where does my strength come from?*
> *My help comes from the Lord, the Maker of heaven and earth. He will*
> *not let your foot slip - he who watches over you will not slumber.....*
> *He will watch over your life; the Lord will watch over your coming and*
> *going both now and for evermore.'*
> *Psalm 121 v 1-3 & 7-8*

I prayed a lot leading up to my consultant appointment, and on the whole felt fairly calm and peaceful. I hadn't really told anybody outside my close family up to this point. The day of my appointment arrived and my youngest sister, Louise, was able to stay with me for an hour before she had to go to work. Unfortunately, my name hadn't been called by the time she had to leave, nor for another hour afterwards. The butterflies were swirling in my stomach.

I was at the hospital for over five hours that day, and had to go back again the next day for a further biopsy. The consultant I saw struggled to get a biopsy sample as the lump was so far back that she was afraid of piercing my lung. The senior consultant was left-handed and apparently therefore would be more able to reach it if I came back the following day! I'm rather fond of my lungs, so on that basis was happy for the first consultant to abandon the process and for me to return the next day.

Again I was struck by how hard it is to wait and to be tested further. After hours spent at the hospital in this department and that (and I haven't mentioned the dreaded mammogram that reminded me so much of woodwork at school when an object is squeezed tightly into the vice - ouch!), there was more to come. More waiting, more testing, more pain. But again, I was so aware of God's presence with me - holding me, strengthening me, comforting me. It's almost as if his presence could be physically touched. As I sat on the bed waiting for the consultant on the second day (why do they call you into the consulting room then make you wait there for ages too?!), I had such a sense of Jesus sitting right there next to me - just quietly, waiting in the stillness; holding my hand when no-one else was there.

God, I praise you that you are always with me.
Wherever I go, I cannot escape from your presence.
You are with me in the waiting and in the testing
Be with me in the waiting room of my life - when uncertainty
is all around me.
Help me to trust you when I don't know what is happening
Fill me, Lord, with your peace and help me not to be afraid.
Amen

'O Lord, you have searched me
and you know me.
You know when I sit and when I rise;
you perceive my thoughts from afar.
You discern my going out and my lying down;
you are familiar with all my ways......
Where can I go from your Spirit?
Where can I flee from your presence?
If I go up to the heavens, you are there;
if I make my bed in the depths, you are there.
If I rise on the wings of the dawn,
if I settle on the far side of the sea,
even there your hand will guide me,
Your right hand will hold me fast.'
Psalm 139 v 1-3 & 7-10

Chapter 4
A Word from the Great Physician

After my second biopsy, I asked the consultant how serious the situation looked and he told me straight that there was cause for concern. In my heart I just knew it was cancer and that it was going to be serious. I remember getting upset and the lovely breast care nurse making me a cup of tea and saying that I must not walk out of the room giving myself a diagnosis, as nobody knew until the results came back.

Unlike the previous day, the church intercessors were praying for me on this day. Our church intercessors are a group mainly of ladies who meet every Wednesday morning, and they are total prayer warriors and women of faith. Their prayers that day made such an amazing difference and again the presence of God was tangibly with me. I felt crushed, lost, scared and alone but had incredible peace and strength within me, not from myself but which I can only describe as being from God.

> *'My grace is sufficient for you,*
> *for my power is made perfect in weakness.'*
> *2 Corinthians 12 v 8*

Despite feeling broken, I know God was giving me strength because my sister, Louise, was having a pregnancy scan in the same hospital, at the same time. I went to find her after my appointment and though I had missed the scan, the nurse very kindly took us back into the scan room and showed me the baby as her next patient had not arrived. Louise's joy and excitement was infectious at the sight of her unborn child, and I celebrated with her, concealing what I had just been told. I couldn't bear to spoil such a special occasion, so I just told her I would have the results the following Monday. Again, God was giving me his amazing mix of strength and grace.

When I saw my dad later, I told him what the consultant said and broke down in his arms. He hugged me tightly and we cried together. It was so lovely to be held by my dad, and I just stayed there in his arms for such a long time. It was as though my heavenly father was holding me too, and maybe he was crying as well.

The hardest parts about that day were telling Ian when he was on a street in New York, and not telling the boys. I felt so sad for my husband, as he was so very far away, when we should have been together. Again God must have been giving me strength because I remember Ian saying that he would try and be strong, only because I was being so strong and calm. I tried to 'be normal' with the boys, as the nurse had advised me not to say anything to them, because the worst thing for children is uncertainty. I felt as if I was keeping a massive secret, but had to respect what she had said, so I said nothing. They didn't even question their dad coming home from America a week early.

That night when the boys were in bed, I was having my daily quiet time and reading my Bible. I read UCB's 'Word for Today', which gives a verse each day and a comment about it. Amazingly, the verse for the day was about worry.

'Cast your burden on the Lord, and he shall sustain you.'
Psalm 55 v 22

'Do not be anxious about anything, but in everything by prayer and petition, with thanksgiving, present your requests to God. And the peace of God, which transcends all understanding, will guard your hearts and your minds in Christ Jesus.'
Philippians 4 v 6 & 7

The comments talked about how, as Christians, we do not need to worry, because God knows all of our worries and he watches over us always. Worry doesn't change or solve anything - it just creates turmoil within us. Worry needs to be changed into prayer. The passage referred to another Bible verse in 1 Peter chapter 5, which I also looked up:

'Cast all your anxiety on him because he cares for you.'
1 Peter 5 v 7

Sometimes when I read the Bible, a verse or line will jump out at me, as if the Holy Spirit pours a giant beacon on a particular phrase. It reminds me of watching a 3D movie and I always laugh at the cinema when the whole audience leaps back as a ball or space ship or something, comes flying out of the screen. That's just what happened as I continued to read 1 Peter 5 and came across verse 10:

'And the God of all grace, who called you to his eternal glory in Christ, after you have suffered a little while, will himself restore you and make you strong, firm and steadfast.'

And that was it. In that moment, I felt as though God - the great and knowing physician - was giving me his own diagnosis. I just knew in my heart that my gut reaction following the consultant's words, was true, and that I really did have cancer. The results next week almost didn't matter, because in that moment, I just knew. But God was not only giving me a diagnosis, but a promise as well. A promise that any suffering would be for a time, for a period, and then it would be over. A promise that I would be restored, and that one day I would be strong, firm and steadfast. A promise that - for me and for now - I would recover, and that he would see me through it.

That verse has been an amazing inspiration to me over many months of treatment. At times I have felt so weak and sick - a million miles from being restored and strong - but I have held on to that verse as the truth and the words that God spoke to me that night. God's word really is a rock that we can stand on - living and breathing - but firm and unmoving. As Jesus said:

'The words I have spoken to you are spirit and they are life.'
John 6 v 63

Praise God for his word to us!

Lord if this is what you have planned for my life,
if you have decided to allow this diagnosis and treatment to
**   happen to me, then I accept that this is part of your plan for me.**
I'm terribly afraid of what will happen, of months of suffering
**   ahead, but I trust you completely and know that my life is in**
**   your hands.**
I pray that you will bring good out of this situation.
I pray that you will use me to help others like me.
I pray that your will be done and that you use me for your glory.
Amen

Chapter Five
News to Shake Your Very Roots

The next few days passed by in a blur. I worked, looked after the boys and tried to keep life normal. I got upset when Ian came home a week early from his trip to America, as it made the day of my results all the more real and near. Again the boys had no idea why their dad had come home early and didn't even ask.

Some Christian friends from church phoned me. I told them about the verse God had given me and how I believed God had already given me his diagnosis. Some were shocked and didn't really know what to say to this. Everyone encouraged me and said they were praying for me and the family.

On Sunday, Ben, my eldest son, noticed my name was on the 'sick list' for prayer on the church newsletter, and asked me why. I said it was about the tests I had had at hospital last week (which he knew about) and the church were praying for me because I was going for the results the next day. He quizzed me a little about what the results could show, and I desperately tried to distract him before the tears could start.

At the end of the service, there was a call for prayer, and Ian and I went up to the front to be prayed for. A wonderful prayer warrior from the prayer group, Carol, prayed a most beautiful prayer for us. I can't even remember what she said now, but I was really touched by her kind and powerful words. At the end, she prayed for clear results the following day, though again in my heart I just knew that they would not be clear and that I would be given the diagnosis of cancer. It wasn't that I was being pessimistic and downtrodden; I just believed in my heart that God had already told me, and was preparing me for the confirmation.

That night was a somewhat restless one. I remember wondering if that was the last day of my life without cancer and if things would change forever the next day. The day of the results finally arrived - March 22nd - exactly one month after my 40th birthday. How my life could change in one month! In the blink of an eye, everything was different.

Ian and I had to wait almost two hours to be seen at the hospital that morning, and I can quite honestly say they were two of the hardest and longest hours of our whole lives. I felt so nervous, sick and tense, flicking through one tacky magazine to the next, not really taking anything in and not talking much either (which is unusual for me as Ian would tell you!). Eventually, when it seemed that most other people in the waiting room had gone home, my name was called. This was it.

The consultant got straight to the point and started by saying he hadn't been sure last week if there was cancer present or not. For a moment, my heart stopped and I thought, maybe I had been wrong? Maybe it was a false alarm after all and even though I had been so utterly convinced, maybe my life would be spared this? He then paused... however... the test results have confirmed that there is cancer present in the breast. Ian almost broke down beside me. He was utterly shocked, and went silent and as white as a sheet. I, for some reason which can only be down to God, stayed calm and started to ask questions. I've often wondered about how people cope in times of bad news, and there seems to be a strength hidden inside us all that we call upon in times of trouble. The human spirit is strong, but when that spirit is filled with God, then his strength takes over, and makes us even stronger.

The questions and answers continued... mastectomy... chemotherapy... possible radiotherapy... Tamoxifen. All foreign words that had never entered my life before but would become an unyielding reality. Even then, God held me and kept me calm. I had hoped for the best case scenario of a lumpectomy and radiotherapy, but it looked as though a mastectomy would be best, and this would definitely be followed up by chemotherapy.

I went to the toilet on the way out and just prayed. I didn't cry then and I wasn't really shocked. Incredibly, part of me was saying 'Bring it on, Lord. We can cope together. I accept this is your plan for me.' Such bravery fizzled out well and truly over the coming days and weeks, but for then, I was strong.

Ian and I walked back to my sister Jan's house, where we had parked, in stunned silence, not really knowing what to say or think. However, when I saw Jan, I just said "It's bad news" and we broke down together - hearty, snotty sobs on each other's shoulders, not really believing it could possibly be true. My dad came to my sister's house after I phoned to tell him, and we had more hugs and sobs together. I haven't seen my dad cry very often, but he cried that day and that really upset me to see how upset he was. I felt guilty for upsetting everyone around me, and felt bad that my diagnosis would bring back all the painful memories of my mum having cancer.

My sister sent me a text later to say her beautiful son, Sam (then aged four), had asked her why she was crying and was it because she missed Auntie Helen. He told her he would get the phone and ring me so that his mum wouldn't be sad any more. How sweet the way children's minds work!

The hardest part of that day was undoubtedly telling my two lovely boys, and the memory of that conversation will never leave me. Thankfully, Ian did the talking. He's always been good at saying the right thing at the right time, and knowing what to say and what not to. We gathered Ben and Oliver on the conservatory settee, and Ian explained that I had been to the hospital for the results and that I had an illness that we needed to tell them about. I had wondered before, whether they were too young to be told, at only eleven and eight, but decided that I couldn't go through all the treatment without them knowing what was going on. Little did I know at that time, how great their support for me would be, and thus what I could potentially have missed out on, by not telling them.

Ian talked about 'the illness' and how God would help us, and my children's anxious faces became more and more concerned about what he could mean. Eventually, when they kept asking what it was, Ian told them their mum had breast cancer. Stunned silence. Oliver's first words were "Don't people die of that?" His childhood innocence and honesty cut through the silence like a knife, and Ben and I broke down crying. Ben couldn't look at me initially, and fell into his dad's arms asking "Will she be alright? Is mum going to be alright, Dad?" Oli just held me, hugging me tight into his little, thin body. He didn't cry but just kept saying "Ah... ah Mum." Eventually, we swapped boys and Ben and I cried a lot together, hugging tightly.

Amazingly, the boys calmed down and a little later they went to play at their friend's house, down the road. I was pleased at their acceptance and resilience, and glad that they could do something normal rather than just sit and be sad. Children are often surprising in how they cope with bad news, accept it and move on. I know God was with them, strengthening and comforting them that evening, as he has been throughout the journey.

The boys' absence for an hour allowed Ian to begin the round of phone calls to tell family and friends our news, and ask for their prayers. I remember just listening - often hearing his voice tremble and crack as he spoke to his sister, brother and friends - and thinking how hard this was for him to do, and how it is often harder for the partner to watch. I prayed for Ian then, that God would help and strengthen him as he stood by me, probably often feeling helpless next to me, as we began the journey together.

I DO NOT KNOW WHAT LIES AHEAD

'I do not know what lies ahead,
the way I cannot see;
yet one stands near to be my guide,
he'll show the way to me:

I know who holds the future,
And he'll guide me with his hand;
With God things don't just happen,
everything by him is planned.
So as I face tomorrow,
with its problems large and small,
I'll trust the God of miracles,
Give to him my all.

I do not know how many days
Of life are mine to spend;
But one who knows and cares for me
Will keep me to the end.

I do not know the course ahead,
what joys and griefs are there;
but one is near who fully knows,
I'll trust his loving care.'

(Hymn by Alfred B Smith & Eugene Clarke, 1947)

Lord, I am yours.
Help me.
Amen

Chapter Six
Feel the Love!

In the two weeks following my diagnosis and before my scheduled surgery, I experienced a rollercoaster of emotions, the first of which was shock. I remember listening to Ian on the phone to my manager at work the day after my diagnosis, and just thinking, "That's me he's talking about! Me - Helen Jones - and I've got cancer!" Even though I had lost one of my best friends to the disease only eight months earlier, and even though my mum had died of cancer and other members of our extended family had been diagnosed, I still didn't believe it would happen to me. Especially not at only forty years of age - I just felt far too young. I suppose at the back of my mind, I thought I might get it in my fifties or sixties, but not now and certainly not at forty.

As the news of my diagnosis spread among family, friends and work colleagues, so did the shock. A little like throwing a stone into a lake, Ian and I took the brunt of the fall, but waves of disbelief and compassion rolled out among the wider circle of people we knew and loved. The reaction of people around me was incredible, and I was stunned and greatly moved by their compassion. I remember when my friend, Jill, died the previous summer, her funeral was absolutely packed out with people. Another friend, Ellen, and I were talking after the service and we said that Jill never realised how very much she was loved. What a shame - I thought that was tragic. People's reactions to my diagnosis showed me in a very real and often overwhelming way, how very loved I was (I don't know why), and I am really grateful for that opportunity and experience.

Over the next few days, I was constantly receiving texts which conveyed people's shock, coupled with encouragement and support. For me, this was a great way to be in touch with people as I was too upset to talk on the phone. From church friends, university friends, cousins, work mates, and even the boys' football coach, messages of love and support poured in. Here are a sample of the texts I received:

1. From Becca - one of my best friends from university. I'd asked her to pray for us but hadn't said why, so she didn't know at this point: 'You are in our thoughts today. Praying that as a son and daughter of an everlasting father, you

will know him close to you in a new level of his love and grace in your lives. And as heirs with Christ, you will know the reality of his authority and victory in your lives. You have been ordained by God and he has plans to prosper and not to harm you.'

2. From my sister, Jan, before the news: 'Just wanted to say that I am here for you whatever the results are today and I will help and support you in every way I can. Love you big sis.'

3. From my sister, Louise: 'I don't know what to say to make you feel better. It's an awful time for you. Try to keep the positives in mind. I wish I could make everything better for you. If you need me, I'm here.'

4. From my cousin, Annie: 'Ride the rollercoaster honey in the way that suits you - I don't think there's a right or wrong way to deal with this. I'm bending the fella up there's ears on a regular basis for you.'

5. From my brother-in-law, Stuart: 'Helen I am really sorry to hear your bad news. The odds are stacked in your favour, with your age etc, though I am sure it does not feel like that right now. You have an amazingly supportive family that love you and yours, and your faith is strong. Now is the time to let people repay you for your kindness and all you have to do is change the habit of a lifetime and ask for support - we will always be there for you, Ian and the boys. You know where we are. Be strong.'

'Be strong' - that was one of the overwhelming messages I received and I knew it was right, for my children's sake as much as anything. The problem is that often when we receive 'bad news' we automatically become weak and vulnerable, and are stripped of our strength because of the fear that grips hold of us. I know that God was protecting me from fear at this stage, and giving me his own strength. My desire and determination to protect my children from fear and worry, also convinced me that I needed to stay strong throughout the forthcoming days and weeks.

> *'It is God who arms me with strength*
> *… he enables me to stand on the heights.'*
> *Psalm 18 v 32 & 33*

> *'Look to the Lord and his strength;*
> *seek his face always.'*
> *1 Chronicles 16 v 11*

As well as texts, I received so many cards - 'Get Well' and 'Thinking of You' cards, full of messages of love, concern and support. There were so many words of encouragement and kindness that I could fill this whole book with them! Reading every card was like standing in a hot shower and feeling love pour all over me. Many cards expressed the unfairness of my situation, but talked about hope for the future and for my recovery. What struck me was that so many cards, from Christian and non-Christian friends, recognised my faith, and that the strength of my faith would get me through this whole experience. I was really touched by that and thought that even when I don't see it, others must see the light of Christ living in me, and know he is my strength.

Many of the cards contained verses of Scripture, which greatly encouraged me. Here is a selection:

'The Lord is my strength and my song.'
Exodus 15 v 2

'The Lord watches over all who love him.'
Psalm 145 v 20

'I will make a road in the desert and rivers in dry land.'
Isaiah 43 v 19

'The Lord gives strength to his people.'
Psalm 29 v 11

'God cares for you.'
1 Peter 5 v 7

'The Lord is good, a stronghold in days of trouble.'
Nahum 1 v 7

'Hide me in the shadow of your wings until the danger has passed.'
Psalm 57 v 1

So many more verses reminded me of God's vast love and his watchfulness over me. I knew he would be with me and would walk alongside me through whatever the coming weeks and months could throw at me. He would be my strength and my peace.

The bouquets, chocolates and presents also kept pouring in, and at one point I had so many bunches of flowers, that I had to cut up lemonade bottles to serve as vases! I was also struck by how many people were praying for me. I had emails from Australia, messages from America, was on the 'sick list' not only in our church but many others, where friends and family attended. Catholic friends were lighting candles for me, and my aunty and uncle arranged a mass for the day of my surgery, which I was really touched by. I don't think I have ever been prayed for as much in my entire life! I honestly believe that it was all of this prayer that upheld and strengthened me in those early days. Of course, I had sad and shocked days, but I also felt God's amazing peace seep into every part of my being and it was he who strengthened me, not only every day, but every moment of every day. His peace and presence were tangible and more real than ever before.

My good friend from work, Ursula, phoned me often, and each time she said to me "Feel the love!" She told me so many people at work - colleagues, parents, children, teachers - were shocked at my diagnosis, and just wanted to convey messages of support to me. That is just what I felt during this time - an overwhelming sense of love from my family, friends and all those around me - but also a sense that I was totally loved by God, and that he would care for me and carry me through.

I had a sense of being swaddled in God's love - totally safe and warm, and knowing he would protect me. One of my cards from a friend said; 'May the Lord wrap you and surround you in his love' - and that is just how I felt.

Chapter Seven
Before the Surgery

I remember studying the stages of grief at work, largely in relation to parents' reactions to a diagnosis of deafness in their child. Initially, there comes shock and denial, followed by anger. Although I was in shock after my diagnosis, I don't think I denied that this was happening, and I didn't feel angry - not at God or at life. I knew breast cancer was incredibly common and affects a massive one in eight women in the UK, at some point in their lives. Again, I also had a strong conviction that my life was and is in God's hands. For some reason, he had ordained this difficult path for me to walk, but I had a firm assurance that he would walk it with me.

I do remember feeling some guilt though, and once asked Ian if he thought I could have caused it. I wondered if my often stressful life - working in the NHS and caring for the boys while Ian was frequently away - could have caused those cells to form and divide. Or perhaps I hadn't eaten enough fruit and vegetables, and had instead chosen chocolate and red wine. Had I eaten too much tinned food? Used bleach and other cleaning products too often? Was my mobile phone to blame? Perhaps it was due to not getting enough exercise or maintaining my gym membership? Was there something harmful in my deodorant? So many questions and feelings of guilt flitting in and out of my thoughts! Ian told me that I should not blame myself, and that there was often no reason why cells become cancerous. Also, many very healthy women, including some sporting celebrities, had the same disease, so their ultra healthy lives had not been able to prevent it. I felt slightly reassured by this, though did decide that after all of my treatment was over, I needed to live a much more healthy lifestyle.

> *Lord, I'm sorry if I have not looked after my body enough.*
> *I am sorry if I have any part in this diagnosis.*
> *Please free me from any guilt I have.*
> *You created me and gave me this body.*
> *Help me look after it and honour you.*
> *Amen*

'Do you not know that your body is a temple of the Holy Spirit, who is in you, whom you have received from God? You are not your own; you were bought at a price. Therefore honour God with your body."
1 Corinthians 6 v 19 & 20

Before my surgery, I had two weeks to decide if I wanted a mastectomy or a lumpectomy. The consultant had said I could choose, but when I asked which he would recommend, he said a mastectomy as there was no guarantee a lumpectomy would be enough and I may end up needing a mastectomy anyway. I always thought this would be a straightforward, easy decision, but it wasn't and I procrastinated for a while. I felt sad about losing a part of my body, a part of my femininity. I'm not very keen on my body - it's a bit too flabby, with cellulite legs and a big tummy, but I've always thought I had a decent chest. I worried that I would be deformed and resent my own appearance. However, with much prayer and many tears, I decided to be brave and accept that a mastectomy would be best. This would totally remove the cancerous tumour and reduce the risk of reoccurrence in the future. I had to think of my children and whatever would keep me around for as long a part of their lives as possible, was what I had to do.

Before the surgery, I had to attend pre-operative and other hospital appointments. At every opportunity, I spoke to the doctors and nurses about my faith, saying that I believed God would be with me and would help me through the future months of treatment. I probably had 'mad, psycho Christian woman' written on my file! It was something that came so naturally, so easily, as if any other way of coping (i.e. without God) was inconceivable. I've often struggled to speak openly about my faith, and often feel as if I am a rubbish witness to the Lord. However, speaking about God's help throughout this experience, has naturally interlocked with talking about my diagnosis - the two have just gone together hand in hand. In some ways, talking about my faith and how God has upheld me, has helped other people to cope with the shock of my diagnosis.

'Make the most of every opportunity... Let your conversation be always full of grace, seasoned with salt, so that you may know how to answer everyone.'
Colossians 4 v 5 & 6

'Always be prepared to give an answer to everyone who asks you to give the reason for the hope that you have. But do this with gentleness and respect.'
1 Peter 3 v 15

I went into work before my surgery, only a few days after my diagnosis, mainly because there were so many loose ends to tie up and reports to write, before I went off for several months. I think a lot of people were shocked to see me, but again God gave me strength to face people and to talk openly about my diagnosis and surgery. This was again coupled with a testimony as to how God's grace and strength were getting me through each day. I told some people about the verse God had given me from 1 Peter 5 v 10 about suffering, but it only being for a while, and how this verse had given me strength and hope already. Some colleagues said they thought they had a Bible in their houses, and would look it up when they got home! That was a real encouragement to me! I was already seeing how God could use every situation for good.

'And we know that in all things God works for the good of those who love him, who have been called according to his purpose.'
Romans 8 v 28

The Sunday before my surgery was Easter Sunday, which is always a fantastic celebration in our church. I remember the praise and worship being awesome that day as we celebrated Jesus' resurrection. The final song was 'I will sing the wondrous story.'

I will sing the wondrous story
Of the Christ who died for me –
How He left the realms of glory
For the cross of Calvary.

Yes, I'll sing the wondrous story
Of the Christ who died for me –
Sing it with His saints in glory,
Gathered by the crystal sea.

I was lost; but Jesus found me,
Found the sheep that went astray,
Raised me up and gently led me
Back into the narrow way.

Days of darkness still may meet me,
Sorrow's path I oft may tread;
But His presence still is with me,
By His guiding hand I'm led.

He will keep me till the river
Rolls its waters at my feet;
Then He'll bear me safely over,
Where the loved ones I shall meet.

Francis H Rawley 1886

As I sang the song, tears rolled down my cheeks and I had a picture of myself in heaven, standing by this crystal sea, with two breasts! I felt as though God were assuring me that though this operation had to happen, I would be restored in his kingdom and that one day, when I meet him in heaven, I would be given a new, different and perfect body.

The week of my surgery, I was due to go to Spring Harvest in Skegness - a wonderful Christian week of worship and Bible teaching, with my boys, dad, aunty Joy and my friend, Ellen. Unfortunately, my surgery was scheduled for the Thursday of our Tuesday to Sunday stay, so it was not worth me attending. I was gutted, as it is always a really encouraging and inspirational week. My friend decided not to go either, but my dad and aunty Joy took Ben and Oliver. This was again great timing, because although my dad was incredibly sad to leave me to have surgery, the boys were excited at the opportunity, distracted from what was happening and well cared for away from home. There were a few tears as we said goodbye and they drove away, but I knew they would all have a fantastic time.

The day before my surgery, I had to go for sentinel node imaging. A dear friend from church, Marjorie, who herself had recently been diagnosed with cancer, sent me a text that morning saying: 'Remember every day Jesus holds your right hand and he never leaves you'. Later, as I lay down in a huge tubular X-ray machine, with radioactive dye injected into my chest, while doctors plotted my sentinel nodes like mapping treasure, I remembered Marjorie's text. I lay totally still, with my right arm stretched out, as they plotted and drew on my skin with black marker pen. As I lay there, I pictured Jesus sat at the end of the machine, holding my right hand. I felt incredibly close to him, as if I could reach out and touch him, his presence was so very real.

Later that evening, as I was buried in a sea of cooking (a mad idea to make and freeze lots of meals for coming days and weeks), Ian hugged me and said he was getting nervous. I told him I felt nervous too, but everything would be ok. He went on to expand that he said he was nervous because the match was kicking off in half an hour!! His beloved Manchester United were in the UEFA Champions League against Bayern Munich! Men!!

Chapter Eight
The Operation

After hours of cooking and cleaning the kitchen the night before, I was shattered when I finally went to bed and somehow, by God's grace, I had a reasonable night's sleep. I had set my alarm for 6.00 a.m. as I was allowed to drink some water then. I thought I could be waiting for hours before my operation, and from previous experience, always had a banging headache while fasting before surgery. I treated myself to two whole glasses of water (which I later got told off for!).

I had been worrying about the state of my hair as I wasn't allowed to use any hair products - wax or hairspray, so expected to give the nurses a fright at the sight of me! Luckily, the wildness of the hair was calmed slightly by the straighteners, though I still felt horrid without being allowed to wear deodorant either (don't stand too close!).

That morning, I prayed a lot for the doctors and the surgical team who would be carrying out my operation.

Lord, I commit to you this day.
I pray for every nurse, doctor and surgeon who looks after me.
Thank you for them and for their expertise.
Help the surgeons especially, Lord.
Give them skill and attentiveness in their work.
May the operation go well and all happen as planned.
Help them to totally remove this tumour and all traces of cancer
*   from me.*
Thank you for all the medical advances, knowledge and skill that
*   makes this possible.*
Will you dwell in that operating theatre, Lord - watching and
*   guiding; helping and protecting.*
May there be angels all around, ministering your strength.
Walk hand in hand with me through this day, Lord, and bring your
*   healing and peace, I pray.*
In Jesus' name, Amen

Ian and I arrived nervously at the hospital for 7.30 a.m. and he was only allowed to stay until I got checked in. I again felt relatively calm and matter of fact about things, though there was a part of me that felt really sad saying goodbye to my right boob.

Unfortunately one of my worst fears was realised - a big one that I had been fretting about - and that was that I would have to wait hours and hours for a cup of tea. Anyone who knows me, knows that I am just like my dear nan - a total tea addict. I love tea and drink loads of it! The nurses told me that I was LAST on the surgery list for the whole day and that my consultant was doing a big four hour operation before me!!!! Why did I have to be at hospital for 7.30 a.m., I asked?! They told me that I had to be there in case another operation was cancelled. Great! More waiting!

So I sat and waited, in my theatre gown with the openings at the front flashing everything to the world; with my boiling hot fluffy dressing-gown and mega-tight, white, anti-DVT stockings, sweating somewhat - not a very attractive sight!! While I waited, I read a fantastic Christian book that one of my best friends from university, Fran, had sent me about fear. It was called 'Fear Not - For I Am With You Always' by Max Lucado. The verses from the Bible and thoughts/ poems that I read were again so timely and spoke deeply to my spirit. Here is a selection:

'I am with you always, to the very end of the age.'
Matthew 28 v 20

'"Don't be afraid", (Jesus) said.
Take courage. I am here."'
Matthew 14 v 27

'Be of good courage, and he shall strengthen your heart,
all you who hope in the Lord.'
Psalm 31 v 24

'Be strong and brave.
Don't be afraid… and don't be frightened,
Because the Lord your God will go with you.

He will not leave you or forget you.'
Deuteronomy 31 v 6

'Be anxious for nothing, but in everything by prayer and supplication,
with thanksgiving, let your requests be made known to God; and the
peace of God, which surpasses all understanding, will guard your
hearts and minds through Christ Jesus.'
Philippians 4 v 6-7

I was really encouraged by reading this book and God's word, and told some of the nurses about the peace God was giving me. I started chatting to another lady waiting for an operation, and it turned out that she was a Christian too, so we agreed to pray for each other. I chatted to a few people whilst waiting all those hours and many asked how I was so calm before such an awful operation. I told them it was just God - he was with me and was giving me his peace.

Eventually, just before four o'clock, with my throat so very dry, my head now banging due to dehydration and my heart pounding, my name was called to go down to the operating theatre. As I walked through the hospital, along the corridors in my white flowing dressing gown, up in the lift, with a nurse at my side, I had an overwhelming feeling that I was a bride of Christ. What a strange thing to think just before major surgery. Yet when I reflect on it, there couldn't be a more intimate message of love from Jesus than to tell me I was his bride - utterly loved, chosen and walking hand in hand with Christ.

'As a bridegroom rejoices over his bride,
so will your God rejoice over you.'
Isaiah 62 v 5

The book of Revelation talks about the wedding of the Lamb, when Christ will be joined with his bride, the Church. In those final moments before my surgery, I was reminded that one day, I would be part of Christ's bride, united with him in heaven. If I am honest, there was also a slight part of me that hoped that wasn't too soon and that I would actually wake up from the anaesthetic!!

'Let us rejoice and be glad and give him glory!
For the wedding of the Lamb has come, and his bride has

made herself ready.
Fine linen, bright and clean was given her to wear.
(Fine linen stands for the righteous acts of the saints).'
Revelation 19 v 7 & 8

'I saw the Holy City, the new Jerusalem, coming down out of heaven
from God,
prepared as a bride beautifully dressed for her husband.'
Revelation 21 v 2

Feeling reasonably calm and very loved by God, I lay down on the bed in the anaesthetic room, praying quietly. I had a last peek under my theatre gown, at my right boob - almost a goodbye look - then thanked the doctors for looking after me. I continued to pray and thank God for his presence as the doctors inserted the anaesthetic. My arm started to go cold and within seconds, I was asleep.

Anaesthetics are weird and wonderful things! It always amazes me how you can be so deeply asleep and unconscious for doctors to perform surgery, and that you have absolutely no recollection or awareness of what is going on. Thank the Lord for them!!

The operation took around two and a half hours and I spent an hour in the recovery room. When I woke up I immediately felt a searing pain in my chest. I was extremely groggy from the anaesthetic, but managed to ask for some pain relief and was given morphine, which promptly sent me back to sleep. I'll never forget Ian's anxious face when my bed was pushed up to the ward around 7.30 p.m. It must have been a long, worrying day for him and it showed. He was really upset at the sight of me (I knew my hair looked bad though I'm sure the drains and drips didn't help!) and he kept kissing my head and stroking my hair. I was so glad to see him, and relieved that the operation was over and that he was with me. I'm not sure how long he stayed, as I kept falling asleep and drifting in and out of consciousness, but it felt like a long time. I was extremely thirsty and he fed me lots of water in a cup with a straw. I could hardly lift up my head, let alone sit up.

It was some time after Ian left that I saw a vision on the ward - the tea lady!!!! What a wonderful and welcome sight! I was so desperate for a cup of tea by this point, having not had one since midnight the night before. She gave me a cup of tea, again in a special cup with a straw and started feeding it to me. However, it was boiling hot, so she promised to come back later when it had cooled. The tea sat on my bedside cupboard... and sat... and sat for ages. I couldn't sit up to reach it, or to reach the nurses' button to ask for help, so I just looked at it longingly until I fell back asleep. Eventually, when the lady came back to clear up the cups, she remembered she was going to feed it to me and apologised for forgetting. I drank it cold with her help, and even that tasted wonderful!

I must have slept well that night as the lady in the next bed to me said she thought she was at home all night, because my snoring was just as loud as her husband's! I said it must have been the morphine! I sent a text to one of my best friends, Becca, who I shared a room with for two years at university. Poor Bec - she used to try desperately to get to sleep before me in order to avoid my snoring, and if she wasn't successful she would try to turn me over, pinch my nose and once even put a honey butty on my face - anything to stop the dreadful noise! In my text, I said I'd been reminded of her suffering after the lady's comment on the ward, and that I obviously hadn't improved in all these years!!

That day an auxiliary nurse got me up, washed and changed me and helped me get out of bed. It's a humbling experience allowing another person to wash and dress you, and the start for me personally of a long journey of allowing people to do things for me. I am naturally very independent and stubborn, and as my sister, Jan, has often reminded me, a very bad patient! It was so lovely to have visitors that day, even though I felt groggy. Both my sisters, dad, Ian and my little nephew, Sam, all came to see me. They showered me with gifts - sweets, fruit, magazines etc. and encouragement, and I felt uplifted by their visits.

I chatted to some of the other ladies on the ward who had all had a variety of operations. I helped one lady set up her TV and she asked me how I could be so upbeat after having a mastectomy, as she was feeling very sorry for herself after a more minor operation. I just explained again about my faith and how God was giving me his very real and amazing peace, and that I knew my life was totally in his hands. She asked how I could not be afraid of the future. I confessed that I was nervous about chemotherapy and losing my hair, but again that I knew God would walk with me through every stage and process.

Another lady on the ward who had also had a mastectomy and reconstruction, and was very poorly, told me that she had not told anyone other than her husband that she had breast cancer, including her own son and her siblings.

I was shocked at how she could cope on her own. She told me that this was the second time she had been diagnosed and that her experience the first time left her feeling rejected by so many friends and family members, that she didn't want anyone to know this time. I felt so sad for her and offered to pray for her. She asked how I was coping, especially as I was a lot younger than she was, and so I told her about the comfort and strength God was giving me. I gave her a little card from church with a verse from Zephaniah:

'The Lord your God is with you,
he is mighty to save.
He will take great delight in you,
He will quiet you with his love,
He will rejoice over you with singing.'
Zephaniah 3 v 17

I love that verse about God 'quietening you with his love'. Just as a mother picks up her screaming, hot, anguished baby and rocks and holds it calmly in her loving arms, perhaps singing lullabies and songs about how precious the child is. Eventually the baby calms, and becomes quiet and still, because of the mother's love. That is such a wonderful picture of how God loves us. He holds us when we fret and scream and thrash about. I wrote a poem expressing my need for God to calm me:

Hold me till I'm still, Lord
I know I thrash about
There's much to make me angry
I want to scream and shout.
Hold me in your arms, Lord
I need to rest right there
As you gently rock me
And sing away my cares.
Hold me till I'm still, Lord
I know your love is deep
Brush away my tears, Lord
As in your arms I sleep.

When I left hospital the next day, I gave this lady my phone number and said she could always ring me if she needed someone to talk to, and she didn't have to go through it alone. She agreed to ring me, and we said we would meet for coffee some time, but she never did. I often think about her and wonder how she is. It's so sad that people feel they have to cope on their own at such a traumatic time. For me personally, I had never needed my family and friends more.

Chapter Nine
In the Valley

I left hospital two days after my operation, and was glad to get home. One of the worse things was the drains stitched into my chest and under my arm. These drained blood and water into a pot which I carried round with me in a Batman gift bag, which looked rather funny! The drains were removed after ten days. Yuck! Despite their presence, I really enjoyed a Chinese take away that night, especially after the delights of hospital food!

The day after my discharge from hospital, the boys came home from Spring Harvest. When they saw me, my youngest son Oliver said some really precious words to me that I will never forget. He said, in his child-like bluntness, "Have you only got one boob now, Mum? It doesn't matter. You're still beautiful and I love you." Talk about melting my heart! It brings tears to my eyes now just typing this! My eldest son, Ben, just held me tightly and kept asking if I was ok. I was so touched by my children's tender expressions of love and concern for me, and am so grateful to God for them. If my children can love and accept me so completely and utterly, then how much more must God himself love and accept me! I think our understanding of God's vast love for us is so imperfect and so limited, like looking into a misty reflection, as the Bible says. It is only when we meet him in heaven that we will fully understand all that he is and how very deeply he loves us.

> 'When I was a child, I talked like a child, I thought
> like a child, I reasoned like a child.
> When I became a man, I put childish ways behind me.
> Now we see but a poor reflection as in a mirror;
> Then we shall see face to face.
> Now I know in part; then I shall know fully,
> even as I am fully known.'
> 1 Corinthians 13 v 11 & 12

That Sunday, as I lay in bed, the boys put on a CD they had bought at Spring Harvest. They sang and danced the whole way through it - performing all the actions for me and demonstrating that they knew every word. It was fantastic to watch them praising God with all their hearts, and their praise definitely lifted my spirits. This was such an important lesson for me to learn - that there was a massive power in praising God. Over the coming weeks and months, I often felt so weak and ill, and singing and praising God was the last thing I wanted to do. However, when I put on a praise or worship CD and started singing (or rather croaking) along to it, it shifted my perspective from myself on to how awesome God is. Praising him gave me much strength and encouragement.

Over the next couple of weeks I felt physically dreadful. I lost a lot of blood from the surgery and via the drains, as well as the ever conveniently timed monthly period. I became anaemic and felt exhausted. At the same time I started to have real problems with my right knee. I had twisted my knee a few months earlier (my own fault - dancing in high heels at my work Christmas party!) and for some reason, the problem re-occurred now. The pain in my knee grew and grew so that at one point I could hardly walk. I also sprained muscles in my back and neck, because I was walking and lying awkwardly. My GP gave me pain killers, but I ended up asking Ian to take me to the local hospital walk-in centre because I was in so much pain. While I was there I saw two nurses who were really rude to me and totally uncompassionate. When I explained that I was being treated for breast cancer, they both said on separate occasions - "Why do I want to know that?" or "Why are you telling me that?" I felt like screaming, "Because it's a pretty major thing to be happening to me right now and I've also recently had major surgery!" When we left the hospital that day, I broke down in tears in the car because I was so upset at the callousness of their words. I know I was feeling sensitive, but it made me realise how powerful words are and how careful we should be in our use of them. Often we never quite know what people are going through all around us, and how our words can cut into them sharply, causing deep and long lasting wounds. James wrote about the power of the tongue:

> 'No man can tame the tongue. It is a restless evil,
> full of deadly poison. With the tongue we praise
> our Lord and Father, and with it we curse men,
> who have been made in God's likeness. Out of the same
> mouth come praise and cursing.

My brothers, this should not be.'
James 3 v 8-10

'May the words of my mouth and the meditation of my heart be pleasing in your sight, O Lord, my Rock and my Redeemer.'
Psalm 19 v 14

I remember saying to a friend that I felt as if the devil must be thinking I was coping too well with breast cancer and so now he was giving me some extra complications to really get me down. She laughed as she thought it was funny, but I was deadly serious.

In the six weeks between my operation and starting chemotherapy, I went through a period of feeling intensely sad and downhearted. I think part of this was due to how I felt physically, but also I just felt so sad about losing one of my breasts (even though this would save my life) and the realisation that I actually had cancer.

I remember catching sight of myself for the first time in the mirror during my stay in hospital and just staring sadly at my one remaining breast. I felt as if part of my femininity had been stripped from me and I found it hard to accept myself. When the nurse removed my dressing for the first time, I struggled to look down and even for weeks in the bath, I just couldn't look at myself. I wrote a prayer about how sad I felt during that time:

Sad Days
Lord, sometimes I just feel so sad.
A big well of deep sadness crying out inside me.
It takes me by surprise sometimes, Lord, and tears spring to my
**   eyes.**
Hold me on the sad days, Father.
I know Jesus wept. He felt pain and sadness.
Thank you that you know me and you understand how I feel.
Lord I don't want the devil to steal my joy.
Even in the midst of this, I want to hold on to the joy you have
**   given me.**
Your word says that the joy of the Lord is my strength.
Help me to keep my tear-filled eyes firmly fixed on you, Lord.

To look at the smiling face of Jesus
And to see his teary eyes shining back at me.
Fill me, Lord, with your joy, your peace and your comfort.
Amen

My friend, Marjorie, who was already receiving chemotherapy, sent me a card that talked about 'shutter days'. She is an amazingly inspirational lady who despite going through treatment herself, sent me many cards, prayers and words of encouragement throughout my illness. She said she knew I would have sad days, as she did, but that at the end of the day, I just needed to close the shutters on that day and realise that the next day was a new one, with God's fresh mercies flowing.

'His compassions never fail.
They are new every morning;
Great is your faithfulness.'
Lamentations 3 v 23

Chapter Ten
In the Eye of the Storm

As well as a deep sense of sadness over the weeks after my surgery, I also began to feel a wide range of negative emotions such as fear, worry, lack of self-confidence and feelings of rejection. I have always considered myself to be quite a relaxed, outgoing person, but throughout this time, I felt as if my roots had been shaken and as if I had lost some of that natural confidence, and I became a bit more withdrawn. I felt like a tall tree battered in a strong wind, bending over to just before breaking point; ultimately testing the strength of its roots.

During this time, I found great comfort in reading the Psalms. I love the Psalms and they form one of my favourite books in the Bible. The words written by David and other authors centuries ago, reflected much of what I felt and my desire to hold onto the Lord throughout it all. I knew in my heart that these feelings would pass and that as he had promised, he would walk through it all with me, and restore me one day.

'My tears have been my food day and night.
These things I remember as I pour out my soul.
Why are you so downcast, O my soul?
Why so disturbed within me?
Put your hope in God, for I will yet praise him, my Saviour and my God.
Deep calls to deep in the roar of your waterfalls;
All your waves and breakers have swept over me.
By day the Lord directs his love,
At night his song is with me - a prayer to the God of my life.
I say to God my Rock 'Why have you forgotten me?'
My bones suffer mortal agony.
Why are you downcast, O my soul?
Why so disturbed within me?
Put your hope in God,
For I will yet praise him,
My Saviour and my God.'
Psalm 42 (some verses omitted)

I wrote earlier about how I felt a huge wave of love from the people around me at the time of my diagnosis. The support I have had from my family and friends has been an incredible strength to me. However, there were some friends who, I felt, turned away from me and avoided me, especially just after my diagnosis, and this was hurtful. I've spoken to other cancer sufferers and many have said this happened to them too. I realise now, looking back, that I shouldn't be angry because many people just don't know how to react and what to say when someone is diagnosed with cancer. It's similar to when a family is bereaved - people struggle to find the right words and so may avoid saying anything for fear of upsetting that person or family. It's not because friends don't care or aren't interested, some people just don't know what to say. All the same, it is hurtful when someone crosses over the road to avoid you, as happened to me.

> *'All my longings lie open before you, O Lord;*
> *My sighing is not hidden from you.*
> *My heart pounds, my strength fails me;*
> *Even the light has gone from my eyes.*
> *My friends and companions avoid me because of my wounds;*
> *My neighbours stay far away…*
> *O Lord, do not forsake me.*
> *Be not far from me, O my God.*
> *Come quickly to help me, O Lord my Saviour.'*
> *Psalm 38 v 9-11 & 21-22*

Personally, I also struggled to accept the fact that I actually had cancer. I was given leaflets and books to read, websites to look at, even a Christian book on breast cancer by my dad - but for a time, I just couldn't face looking at any of them. It was the dreaded 'C' word and often we referred to 'my illness' rather than being bold enough to say the word 'cancer'. I'm a massive fan of the Harry Potter books and it reminded me of the characters' great fear of actually speaking the name 'Voldemort', and instead, referring to him as 'He who must not be named'. Again my friend Marjorie was constantly encouraging me, and one of the things she said was that cancer shouldn't be called 'the big C' because actually the big 'C' is 'Christ'.

I also felt sad that I had cancer so young - forty feels far too young an age to be affected by such a serious illness, especially when I found out that eight out of ten breast cancer diagnoses are in women over fifty (www.breastcancercare. org). Even though I sensed already that God would use this experience for his good and to bring good out of it, I still didn't want it to happen and wished it never had. It reminds me of the scene in 'Lord of the Rings' when Frodo Baggins is given the ring by Gandalf the wizard, and sent on a treacherous but necessary journey that only he could do. He told Gandalf that he 'wished the ring had never come to him', and that's just how I felt. But Gandalf's words are very interesting in reply and he says that the ring had come to him, and Frodo now had to decide what to do with it.

Several people at the time of my diagnosis, including one of my managers at work, gave me the same verse in Jeremiah 29 v 11, which is a favourite of mine:

> *"For I know the plans I have for you," declares the Lord, "plans to prosper you and not to harm you, plans to give you hope and a future."*

I hoped that in some way God would use me, perhaps to help other people going through the same experience and I praise him that he does have a plan and a purpose for my life.

The last emotion that I struggled with at this time was fear, and at times I felt consumed by it. I would also worry frequently, which is worse than fear in a way, because it means dwelling on and going over and over those things that concern you. I was often convinced that the cancer had spread, especially with the other pains in my knee and back etc. I was convinced that this was the cause. Even when I went back to the hospital for my results and was told my lymph nodes were clear, I was obviously delighted, but part of me wondered if cancer could spread a different way. I also feared its return, and still often think about that, as I know many cancer sufferers do. I also felt afraid and worried about the impending chemotherapy, what horrors it would bring, and specifically about losing my hair.

Having cancer also makes you think about your own mortality and I at times felt afraid of dying, though I never told anyone. It's a shock to think that you may not have as many years left to live your life as you thought you did, or as much time to do all the things that you ever wanted to do. The part that made me most sad was the thought of leaving my children when they were so very young - and my husband too of course - but there is something so painful about the idea of young children being left without a mum, and it cut me to the core to think that could possibly happen to my boys.

I think in all honesty, although I am afraid of dying young, I'm not afraid of dying. This is because I am convinced that when I die, I will be with the Lord in heaven and there could not be a more wonderful place to be. This is not because I am a good or kind person or because of anything I have done. The absolute best thing I could ever do would never be good enough to get me into heaven because only perfection will do. I can't get in to heaven on my own merit, but I believe I will be there purely because of Christ's death for me on the cross. He died because of my sins and he took my place. It's like travelling to Disney but having no money to buy an entrance ticket. If someone else paid for my ticket, I'd be allowed in. Because I have said sorry for all the wrong things I have done in my life and because I believe that Jesus died for me, rose again and is alive today, I have faith that I'll be with him in heaven.

Around this time, Ian was also feeling somewhat down and struggling to accept our situation. I think he felt sad and angry for me that all this was happening. He was also feeling anxious about his impending selection conference to see if he would be accepted to train as a vicar, which was adding extra stress. Because of our own burdens and sadnesses, we didn't really talk to each other heart to heart, which created a distance between us. In a way we both felt somewhat alone, as we struggled to come to terms with life.

Like huge waves crashing around me, rolling and breaking in my head again and again, were the feelings of sadness, fear, worry and darkness at this time. I felt like one of the disciples on the boat in the storm in Matthew chapter eight, longing for the waves to stop, but Jesus was sleeping and the storm raged on. At just the right time, I read the following beautiful prayer in my 'Word for Today' by UCB:

> *The storms of my life have all but sunk my boat;*
> *I can't take much more.*
> *Prince of peace I need you.*
> *Father who never slumbers nor sleeps, take charge.*
> *I need the comfort and courage that comes from your spirit.*
> *Speak, Lord, for the wind still remembers the sound of your voice.*

Let me find in you a quiet place,
A place where I can pillow my head on your breast,
Hear your heartbeat and feel secure.
Amen
(UCB. 3rd June 2010. Kindly reproduced with permission.)

'He gives power to the weak and to those
who have no might, he increases strength.'
Isaiah 40 v 29

I love the words of the Matt Redman song - 'No You Never Let Go', which assure us that God is right there in the heart of the storm, holding and helping us, whatever trials we are going through.

Even though I walk through the valley of the shadow of death
Your perfect love is casting out fear
And even when I'm caught in the middle of the storms of this life
I won't turn back
I know you are near

And I will fear no evil
For my God is with me
And if my God is with me
Whom then shall I fear?
Whom then shall I fear?

Oh no, You never let go
Through the calm and through the storm
Oh no, You never let go
In every high and every low
Oh no, You never let go
Lord, You never let go of me

And I can see a light that is coming for the heart that holds on
A glorious light beyond all compare
And there will be an end to these troubles

But until that day comes
We'll live to know You here on the earth

Yes, I can see a light that is coming for the heart that holds on
And there will be an end to these troubles
But until that day comes
Still I will praise You, still I will praise you

Beth Redman and Matt Redman
Copyright © 2005 Thankyou Music

**Help my heart to hold on, Lord, and
still I will praise you.
Amen**

Chapter Eleven
In the Heart of the Battle

What I didn't realise throughout this time, was that I was in a spiritual battle as well as a physical one. Physically I felt rough, emotionally I felt drained and battered, but spiritually I felt quiet, weak and subdued. I do believe that the devil exists and that he delights in our weaknesses, of which I have many!

> *'Your enemy the devil prowls around like a roaring lion looking for someone to devour. Resist him, standing firm in the faith.'*
> 1 Peter 5 v 8 & 9

> *'Submit yourselves, then, to God. Resist the devil, and he will flee from you. Come near to God and he will come near to you.'*
> James 4 v 7

During this period of time our vicar, Mark, preached a fantastic sermon about being in a spiritual battle. He talked about there being spiritual forces who work in opposition to those who love the Lord, desiring to turn the Church away from God. He preached about a passage in Daniel which I was not familiar with (Daniel 10). Here Daniel was in mourning, not eating, exhausted and without any strength. An incredible heavenly being - an angel - appeared, touched him and spoke to him. He told Daniel that from the very time he had started crying out to God, his every word had been heard, but that he (the angel) had been delayed getting to him, due to the spiritual battle that was taking place.

> *'Again the one who looked like a man touched me and gave me strength. "Do not be afraid, O man highly esteemed," he said. "Peace! Be strong now, be strong."'*
> Daniel 10 v 18 - 19

I realised that even though I didn't 'feel' great - physically, emotionally or spiritually - God had heard every word that I had cried out. All of my longings and mournings over recent weeks had reached him, even though I had felt as though I was in the boat with him sleeping below deck. He was actually on the deck with me, standing right beside me. Maybe I didn't feel strengthened at that time because of the spiritual battle going on around me, and I needed to get up and join the fight!

Mark's sermon studied Ephesians chapter 6 - 'The armour of God' - and this was a passage that had previously struck me, just before the time of starting my chemotherapy.

> *'Finally, be strong in the Lord and in his mighty power. Put on the full armour of God, so that you can take your stand against the devil's schemes. For our struggle is not against flesh and blood, but against the rulers, against the authorities, against the powers of this dark world and against the spiritual forces of evil in the heavenly realms. Therefore put on the full armour of God, so that when the day of evil comes, you may be able to stand your ground, and after you have done everything, to stand.'*
> *Ephesians 6 v 10-13*

I really felt as if I was in 'the day of evil'. Cancer is like an evil - a growing invisible enemy that destroys people in so many ways, not only physically, but emotionally and often spiritually as well. For myself, it caused me to draw closer to God and cry out for his help, but for some people, an understandable reaction is to become angry and blame God, often turning away from him. I knew I was in a battle against it, and in the future, at the end of the battle, I wanted to still be standing.

> *'Stand firm then, with the belt of truth buckled round your waist, with the breastplate of righteousness in place, and with your feet fitted with the readiness that comes from the gospel of peace. In addition to all this, take up the shield of faith, with which you can extinguish all the flaming arrows of the evil one. Take the helmet of salvation and the sword of the spirit, which is the word of God. And pray in the spirit on all occasions with all kinds of prayers and requests.'*
> *Ephesians 6 v 14-18*

I knew that I had to start putting on the armour that God had given me, and to stand firm in the midst of the battle. Firstly he had given me 'truth'. Medically the truth was that my cancer could be treated and hadn't spread, but that wasn't important. The ultimate truth was that Christ had died to save me and that I could be assured of the eternal love of an everlasting father. I knew the devil could speak lies to me - about the future being bleak, about me not recovering etc but I had to stand on the promise God had given me, before I was diagnosed, of being restored, strengthened, firm and steadfast, one day. Even if this was not the case and my future was medically uncertain, the truth was that God knew every day that was ordained for me; he had created me, loved me and given me life.

God also gave us a breastplate to protect our hearts, and my heart was full of confusing emotions and sadness. I certainly needed to start wearing that breastplate and asking for his protection on my heart! I also needed to maintain that readiness to tell others about what God was doing for me, how he was helping me and giving me his peace, throughout the difficult times. The shield of faith was incredibly important. I felt so many arrows of doubt, worry, fear, depression and sadness being aimed at me that I needed faith to shield their attacks. Faith that my life was God's and that he had a future and a plan for me. I needed the helmet of salvation to protect my mind. Knowing God had saved me and he was in control, shielded my mind from worry and anxiety, though I had to be careful to keep wearing it as the doubts and worries could easily creep back. Lastly, the word of God, the Bible, was probably the most important of all for me at this time, because I needed to use it to slash all the negative attacks that were fired against me. God's word is living and powerful and brought me great comfort, guidance and strength along the way - often just enough for each day.

'Your word is a light to my path.'
Psalm 119 v 105

'The word of the Lord stands forever.'
1 Peter 1 v 25

I've always loved the Bible and when I was seventeen, I made a promise to God that I would read it every day. I think I've stuck to that! When I went to university, I shared a room with Becca, who I've talked about before, and who remains a really good friend to this day. Even now she talks about what an influence on her that was - that even if we'd been out to a party or to the pub and went to bed at 3 a.m., I would always have to read my Bible in bed before I went to sleep. She told me not long after my diagnosis that because I had been so faithful in reading the Bible, and had it written on my heart, I would be like the wise man who built his house upon the rocks (Matthew 7), and when the storm came, the house would stand firm because of its solid foundation. I think that's a fantastic picture and knowing God's word certainly proved to be a firm foundation on which I could stand, but also a weapon for the fight.

> *'No weapon forged against you will prevail.'*
> Isaiah 54 v 17

> *'Who shall separate us from the love of Christ? Shall trouble or*
> *hardship or persecution or famine or nakedness or danger or sword?...*
> *No in all these things we are more than conquerors through him who*
> *loved us. For I am convinced that neither death nor life, neither angels*
> *nor demons, neither the present nor the future, nor any powers, neither*
> *height nor depth, nor anything else in all creation, will be able to*
> *separate us from the love of God that is in Christ Jesus our Lord.'*
> Romans 8 v 35, 37-39

What an amazing promise that is in Romans! No trials, no difficulties, no spiritual battle, illnesses or pain - nothing in all creation can separate us from Christ's love for us. I love the sign for 'separate' in British Sign Language, and I'll try to describe it. Start with the backs of your fingers together (fingertips to the floor), make a strong downward movement and then pull your hands apart (a little like a breaststroke movement). It makes me think of breaking a box open, then pulling it apart. It's as if the devil tries to get in those cracks and push us apart from God, through the trials of life, but he will fail because nothing can separate us from God's love.

Lastly, I think it's important to remember that we are not alone in the battle and that our church and other believers are in it with us. We all stand together - side by side. I strongly believe that the prayers of my church, friends and family - as people stood alongside me, strengthened and encouraged me - made a huge difference. Going back to Mark's sermon on spiritual battles, he showed a picture of the Roman battle formation. This line up is still used today by riot police as being the most effective line of defence.

When believers stand together, dressed in God's own armour, there is no better defence. As for me, at my lowest and weakest points, I felt totally surrounded and protected, right in the middle of the formation, defended by the strength, kindness and prayers of those precious people around me. I thank God for them!

Chapter Twelve
Treatment and Reflections

On 26th May, 2010, I had my first chemotherapy treatment. I think in many ways, the build up and anticipation of chemo, was worse than the actual treatment itself. Many of the waves that battered me in the weeks after my surgery, were of dread and anxiety over the later treatments and side-effects I would face.

Often when I look back at my life, I marvel at God's preparation. People often talk about him weaving a tapestry of our lives; working in all the threads and colours, which we can only view from the wrong way round. God however, can see the whole and complete picture, and plans every thread, using both dark and light colours to create the final work of art.

My life is but a weaving
Between my Lord and me
I cannot choose the colours
He worketh steadily
Oftimes He weaveth sorrow
And I in foolish pride
Forget He sees the upper
And I the underside

Not til the loom is silent
And the shuttles cease to fly
Shall God unroll the canvas
And explain the reason why
The dark threads are as needful
In the Weaver's skillful hand
As the threads of gold and silver
In the pattern He has planned

Benjamin Malachi Franklin (1882-1965)

I've dedicated this book to my dear friend Jill Pennington, who died in 2009. I knew Jill for six years. She was a nurse who worked with the elderly, and had a lovely family of two boys and a husband, John. We met at church and became friends, being part of the same cell group and later leading a cell together. She became interested in signing and grew passionate about it and signing for the deaf in church. I'll never forget the way she signed many worship songs - it was utterly beautiful. Often when we sing songs in church now, I feel the tears welling up in my eyes, as I picture her signing away at the front, full of grace and smiling radiantly. She had an incredible faith and totally loved the Lord. Her Bible was virtually falling apart because of her constant enthusiastic studying of the Scriptures. I didn't know Jill when she had breast cancer for the first time, but she often talked about it. When it returned in 2008, I tried to support her throughout all of the lengthy process. We met often to pray together, and I took her to the wig shop to choose her wig, and out for lunch as often as possible. Though I never took her for her chemotherapy, we would text each other and I would pray for her especially on those days. Jill was a total inspiration both to me and to many other people. She was so upbeat, positive and full of joy, and she would never complain about the treatment she was going through. We often laughed together and her deep hearty laugh still rings in my ears. She showed no fear of cancer or chemotherapy and took everything in her stride. Even in her last weeks she was deeply concerned about other people, even comparatively insignificant things like my son, Oliver's ear infection - and she had total faith in God that he would heal her in his way and time.

I am convinced that knowing Jill and seeing her faith, joy and confidence has helped me hugely to face my own treatment. Knowing that she wasn't afraid and didn't feel sorry for herself, was an example for me to follow. Walking alongside Jill in her trial, helped prepare me and take away a lot of my own fear of cancer and chemotherapy. I had seen God holding her right hand throughout the process, and so now I knew he could and would, hold mine.

'No eye has seen, no ear heard,
no mind has conceived
what God has prepared for those who love him.'
1 Corinthians 2 v 9

Marjorie, who I mentioned earlier, was a mutual friend of mine and Jill's and she said exactly the same thing - that God had put us both alongside Jill, to stand by and support her in her trial, but also to prepare us for our own.

Over the next five months, I received chemotherapy every three weeks. This was given to me as a day patient at my local hospital. I had four doses of epirubicin-cyclophosphamide and four doses of docotaxol. Needless to say, the side effects were gruelling. I suffered with much sickness and nausea with the first four treatments and then a creepy sense of aching in every part of my body (like a severe dose of flu), after each of the last four. Over the five months I became more and more exhausted and often just felt devoid of energy. The side effects tended to last for a week after the first few doses, followed by a well period lasting a couple of weeks until the next cycle. However, towards the end, the side-effects were lasting two weeks and the 'well period' only lasted a week. I'll talk separately about losing my hair in a later chapter, because I found this quite a big deal.

Whereas waves of sadness had washed over me prior to starting chemotherapy, once it was underway, I felt God pouring into me his own healing and strength. Many people said to me throughout the course of treatment, that I 'looked well' and one of the nurses told me after my seventh treatment, that I looked too well to be coming to the cancer ward! I'm convinced that the reason that I 'looked well' (when often I felt physically dreadful) was actually the Holy Spirit within me, causing almost an inner radiance. Several people actually told me I looked 'radiant', though I'm not sure if this was because of how hot and red faced I felt under my wig!

> *'God has poured out his love into our hearts*
> *by the Holy Spirit, whom he has given us.'*
> *Romans 5 v 5*

> *'Those who look to him are radiant; their*
> *faces are never covered with shame.'*
> *Psalm 34 v 19*

> *'Arise, shine, for your light has come,*
> *and the glory of the Lord rises upon you...*

Lift up your eyes and look about you…
Then you will look and be radiant.'
Isaiah 60 v 1, 4 & 5

About half way through my chemotherapy, I was reading a passage in Malachi:

'For he will be like a refiner's fire or launderer's soap.
He will sit as a refiner and purifier of silver;
he will purify the Levites and refine them like
gold and silver.'
Malachi 3 v 2 -3

I started reading the footnotes about the procedure to refine metals and read that basically metal is heated with fire until it melts. That must be incredibly hot! This makes the impurities in the metal separate and rise to the surface, where the refiner skims them off, leaving a purer metal. The metal or gold is then so pure and shiny that the refiner's face is clearly reflected in it.

As I thought about this, I realised that Ian and I were going through the toughest and most intense trial of our lives. Indeed in his Christmas card to me at the end of the year, Ian wrote 'Truly an annus horriblis, and the most challenging and difficult of our lives together.' It was the most intense 'heat' we'd ever felt. But as I reflected on the purifying process, I thought that so many impurities in my life were being raised and removed through such a time - anger, selfishness, impatience, worry, ingratitude, unforgiveness, pride - all raising up and popping like bubbles in a fish tank. Experiencing cancer and its treatments has caused me to think deeply about my life and attitudes. Many previous things that worried and annoyed me, seem so insignificant and trivial now. I wonder why I got stressed about work and home life. I'm also more patient with my boys and my love for them and for Ian, and indeed for all my family, has totally intensified. I'm so thankful to God for all of them! I also have a brighter outlook: I'm so grateful for each day of my life now, whereas before I almost took my life for granted. I also pray more and believe more strongly in the power of prayer.

I love the idea of the refiner's face being reflected in the metal during the heating and purifying process. I love the picture that God himself could be putting his face so very close to me and studying me intently. I hope that in some small way, I can be a reflection of him - of his love, strength, hope and peace.

> *'For you, O God, tested us;*
> *You refined us like silver....*
> *We went through fire and water but you*
> *brought us to a place of abundance.'*
> *Psalm 66 v 10 & 12*

> *'But thanks be to God who always leads us in triumphal procession in*
> *Christ and through us spreads everywhere the aroma of Christ among*
> *those who are being saved and those who are perishing. To the one we*
> *are the smell of death; to the other, the fragrance of life.'*
> *2 Corinthians 2 v 14 -16*

My name 'Helen' comes from the Greek for 'bright one' or 'shining light' and my life's vision is to be that for God. At university, I had a poster on my wall of a beautiful sunset over the sea and it said 'Shine on me Father, that I might reflect your light.' My prayer is that as a result of this trial and fiery process, I might know God more deeply, love him more intensely and reflect him more brightly.

Chapter 13
Help from the Holy Spirit

The six months of chemotherapy seemed endless and just as time can pass so quickly when you are having fun, it can go so incredibly slowly when you are not! I remember thinking in May when it started, that the end of October, when my treatment would finish, felt like a million miles away. However, during this slow, lengthy process as I was medically treated and made well, so it was also a time for me to draw close to God and receive from him. Just as Jesus sent the Holy Spirit to his disciples after his death (Acts 1 & 2), to equip them and strengthen them for the purpose he had assigned for them, I believe it was the Holy Spirit that came and strengthened me.

As a child I was never really sure who the Holy Spirit was exactly, and had a mystical idea that he was God's ghost hovering in the corner of the church. I remember hearing the minister talking about 'the Trinity' - Father, Son and Holy Spirit, but I never quite knew what he meant. As I've grown up, I've come to understand that the Holy Spirit is like the very heartbeat of God. He's a very real, living part of God - who is actually God himself, but is also a separate person. The Holy Spirit is like God's action man - it's through his power that things happen. Last year I read the book 'The Shack' by William Young, which named the Holy Spirit 'Sarayu', and personified him as an Indian lady who was wrapped in beautiful, colourful lights. The Sarayu is actually a river in Uttar Pradesh in Northern India and its name means "air, wind, or that which is streaming". I think that is an excellent explanation of the Holy Spirit - like the breath of God or a river flowing into or through his people. Indeed, when Jesus appeared to his disciples again after his death, he breathed on them as a sign of giving them the Holy Spirit:

> 'Again Jesus said "Peace be with you! As the Father
> has sent me, I am sending you." And with that he
> breathed on them and said , "Receive the Holy Spirit."
> John 20 v 21 & 22

A lot of people have a misconception that the Holy Spirit is only about people speaking in strange languages and falling to the floor. Although those things can happen, the Holy Spirit is so much more. The Holy Spirit shows us that God is alive and he is very much at work today. He was present in the first and last chapters of the bible, and is mentioned through out its writings.

'Now the earth was formless and empty, darkness
was over the surface of the deep, and the Spirit
of God was hovering over the waters.'
Genesis 1 v 2

'The Spirit and the bride say, "Come!"
Revelation 22 v 17

For me, going through chemotherapy was when I felt closest to the Holy Spirit; as if he was living inside me, breathing peace into my mind and heart and simply flowing through me. It was as if, having no strength of my own, he came and gave me strength, perseverance and even joy. The Bible talks about the 'fruit of the spirit' - like a tree planted and growing, the Holy Spirit bears fruit in the places where it dwells.

'But the fruit of the Spirit is love, joy, peace, patience,
kindness, goodness, faithfulness, gentleness and self control.
Against such things there is no law.'
Galatians 6 v 22-23

Just as warmth melts away ice on a wintry window, so I felt that the Holy Spirit came and melted many of the dark, crippling emotions I had felt earlier. This isn't to say that I stopped worrying and felt content all the time - I think often it is natural that worries and concerns come back, but I tried to keep giving all my concerns back to God, each time I felt the ice of my emotions freeze over again.

One of the main fruits of the Spirit that I experienced, was God's peace. It was incredible, tangible and lasting. Peace that could not be explained and that defied the circumstances around me. It would be so easy to be consumed by worry and fear of the future, but God's peace filled me every day. I remember how Jill used to say while she was going through her illness, that she didn't know how people coped who didn't know the Lord, because his peace was so real and important in sustaining her.

> *'Do not be anxious about anything, but in everything, by prayer and petition present your requests to God. And the peace of God, which transcends all understanding will guard your hearts and minds in Christ Jesus.'*
> *Philippians 4 v 6 - 7*

> *'Be still and know that I am God.'*
> *Psalm 46 v 10*

> *'Do not worry about tomorrow'*
> *Matthew 6 v 24*

> *'A heart at peace gives life to the body, but envy rots the bones.'*
> *Proverbs 14 v 30*

Peace is the opposite of worry. Worry is when we dwell on things that concern us, over and over again. My late, beautiful mother-in-law, Jean, was such a lovely lady, but a terrible worrier. She would worry about little things - what time the family would arrive, how long to cook her meat - and it saddened me to see her worry so much. Ironically, when she was diagnosed with lung cancer in 2005, she seemed to stop worrying and found some peace - I hope, pray and believe it was the Lord who helped her through such a terrible time. It doesn't make sense to have peace in your life when terrible things happen, but that is the power of the Holy Spirit who makes the impossible, possible.

Another important part of the help that God gave me, was hope. On the day of my diagnosis, my UCB 'Word for Today' was again perfect timing and was titled 'Keep hope alive.'

> *'These three remain - faith, hope and love.'*
> *1 Corinthians 13 v 13*

> *'You will be secure, because there is hope;*

you will look about you and take your rest in safety.'
Job 11 v 18

'Command those who are rich in this present world not to be arrogant
nor to put their hope in wealth, which is so uncertain, but to put their
hope in God, who richly provides us with everything for our enjoyment.'
1 Timothy 6 v 17

A friend of mine, Liz, once described my breast cancer experience as a 'blip' in my life and after it all, I would be fine. Her matter of fact attitude and encouragement, was one of the many statements that gave me hope. Hope is holding onto the future and looking forward to what that future will bring. I feel that it is so important to stay positive when you go through cancer treatments, and for me God was the source of my positivity because of the hope he gave me.

Just after the start of my chemotherapy, my husband Ian went to a Bishops' Advisory Panel which is a three day assessment programme within the Church of England, to determine if he should be allowed to train for ordained ministry. The Bishops' Advisory Panel (or BAP) was the culmination of a two year application and interview process - believe me, the church doesn't hurry these things! Since the tender age of 11, Ian had wanted to become a vicar. He had applied twice before and been unsuccessful on both accounts, much to our heartfelt disappointment. Ian described his application this time, as not just the 'last chance saloon', but 'last orders in the last chance saloon!' After he had attended the BAP and while we were waiting to hear the result, I read Psalm 37 v 4:

'Delight yourself in the Lord and he will give you the desires of your
heart. Commit your way to the Lord; trust in him and he will do this.'

It had been Ian's heart's desire for many years to become a vicar, and though he had pursued other vocations and business ventures, none had satisfied him because of this desire and hope within him. Since before we were married, I had known this was what Ian wanted, and I also had hope that one day I might become a vicar's wife and have a role in leading a church, perhaps working in children's or women's ministries, alongside Ian. We were therefore absolutely delighted when we found out that he had been accepted and could start training! Unfortunately Ian's training had to be deferred for a year because of my illness and treatment, but we moved to theological college in the autumn of 2011. Although we were nervous about uprooting the boys and leaving everything behind, I knew that God had plans for us because he had kept that hope alive in me throughout the duration of my illness. I've already quoted one of my favourite verses in the Bible, Jeremiah 29 v 11:

> *'For I know the plans I have for you' declares the Lord, 'Plans to prosper you and not to harm you, plans to give you hope and a future.'*

I believe God has plans for each and every one of us. It doesn't have to involve going to theological college and leading a church. God has a role for every single one of his children and desires to share his will with us. The knowledge that he holds our future in his hands and has a plan specifically for us, is an incredible source of hope, and should be an encouragement to each one of us, as we think about our own futures.

The Holy Spirit filled me with so many other things during the times of my chemotherapy - faith, trust, love, strength, encouragement, comfort and joy. My faith definitely deepened in and through this whole experience and I feel that I have a closer relationship with God because of, and at the end of it all. At times during my treatment, I felt far from God and I wanted to trust and have faith in him to be with me and heal me, but these were lacking. I love the words that the father of a sick boy spoke to Jesus in Mark 9 and I made them my prayer at times when I struggled to trust God:

> *'Immediately the boy's father exclaimed, "I do believe; help me overcome my unbelief!"'*
> *Mark 9 v 24 (NIV)*

I love the wording of this in the King James Version of the Bible.

> *'And straightway the father of the child cried out, and said with tears, "Lord, I believe; help thou mine unbelief."'*

In all honesty, we all struggle to trust God at times, especially when things are not going well for us, but he sees the tears that we cry and he helps strengthen our doubts and unbelief. Many other verses about trust and faith encouraged me over the weeks. Here are a selection:

> *'Trust in the Lord with all your heart and lean not on your own understanding; in all your ways acknowledge him and he will make your paths straight.'*
> *Proverbs 3 v 5*

> *'You are my refuge, my portion in the land of the living.'*
> *Psalm 142 v 5*

> *'Our sufficiency is from God.'*
> *2 Corinthians 3 v 5*

> *'He will take care of you.'*
> *Psalm 55 v 22*

At different points in this book, I've already talked about the love and strength I felt from God. Every day, and often just enough for that day, the Holy Spirit would pour into me a sense of his love for me and enough strength to face that day. As part of this, I also felt a great comfort from God. No matter how strong you feel going through cancer, there is an element of sharp sadness, loss and mourning. So often I felt God's very real comfort pour into me - into the hollow places of sorrow that only he could see. There's a fantastic verse about comfort in 2 Corinthians, and I sincerely hope now that I have known God's comfort in this way, I will be able to share it with others.

> *'Praise be to the God and Father of our Lord Jesus Christ, the Father of compassion and the God of all comfort, who comforts us in all our troubles, so that we can comfort those in any trouble with the comfort we ourselves have received from God. For just as the sufferings of Christ flow over into our lives, so also through Christ our comfort overflows.'*
> *2 Corinthians 1 v 3*

A Prayer during Chemotherapy
Lord, thank you for the amazing gift of your Holy Spirit
whom you give to me and leave with me.
Come, Holy Spirit.
Breathe on me and fill every part of my being.
Where there is darkness, come and shine your light
Where there is sadness, come and fill me with joy
Where there is worry, pour in your peace
Where there is weakness, bring your strength
Where there is fear, bring courage and faith
Where there is mourning, bring your comfort
Sustain me, Lord, and keep me going
Keep hope alive in me
Fill me with the Father's love
Amen

One of my mum's favourite songs was 'Make me a Channel of your Peace'. I struggle to sing it now because each time I do, it reminds me of my mum's funeral, where we sang it. I love to sign it though, and often do so for a deaf-blind lady that I interpret for in church (thankfully she can't see my eyes fill with tears!). The signs show how God fills us and pours his Spirit into us and he is then poured out onto those around us. Just as I have known God's strength, peace, comfort, kindness and goodness as I have gone through chemotherapy, my prayer now is that I share these with people around me - themselves going through cancer and other treatments, or all kinds of trials - and indeed that I become a channel for God to use.

Make me a Channel of your Peace

Make me a channel of your peace.
Where there is hatred, let me bring your love.
Where there is injury, your pardon, Lord,
And where there's doubt, true faith in you.

Oh, Master grant that I may never seek
So much to be consoled as to console,

To be understood as to understand,
To be loved, as to love with all my soul.

Make me a channel of your peace.
Where there's despair in life, let me bring hope.
Where there is darkness, only light,
And where there's sadness, ever joy.

Make me a channel of your peace
It is in pardoning that we are pardoned
In giving of ourselves that we receive,
And in dying that we're born to eternal life.

Sebastian Temple
Dedicated to Mrs Frances Tracy.

Chapter 14
Sisterhood!

I started this book talking about my 40th birthday and one of my favourite celebrations was a "girls' night out", when thirteen of us went out for a meal and to a concert/dance. It was a really superb evening, and one of the best nights out I've ever had! As I sat round the table looking at my sisters, sisters-in-law, friends from work and home, I felt so blessed to know them all and to have them in my life. We laughed together, ate together, danced together and sat up talking into the early hours. Needless to say, I had a few red wines to celebrate the occasion, so I also remember feeling rather rough the next day!

Little did I know that only a few weeks after we all danced and celebrated together, we would all be shocked and upset by my diagnosis and we would start the long journey of support through cancer treatment.

Looking back now, I am so grateful to God for my family and friends who have supported me and walked with me through the whole experience. I couldn't have done it without them. Of course, the men in my life were a huge support to me too, but I'm going to talk separately about men in the next chapter, because I do think there is a difference in how women support other women.

So many ladies have stood by me, prayed for me and supported me, that I often feel overwhelmed and undeserving of their love. One person who has been an amazing support at every level and throughout the year of my treatment, is my sister, Jan. Her love for me has been unconditional, totally devoted and sacrificial. She has walked with me through every stage of the process - cried with me at my diagnosis, supported me afterwards, visited me in hospital, taken me for my wig and mastectomy bra fittings, taken care of me when I was ill and weak, looked after me and my children when Ian was away and even when they were ill - to stop me getting infections. She cooked meals for me to eat and freeze, bossed me about when I wasn't resting enough, prayed for me, talked to me and encouraged me. I don't think I could ever repay her for all she has done for me and I will be grateful to her for as long as I live. Whenever I say this to her, she always says it's nothing and only part of being a sister and what I would have done for her, if it was the other way round. When I told her I was writing about her kindness in this book, she even said, "Don't waste your pages!" I know that I would have done the same for her if the roles were reversed, but even so, Jan has gone way beyond the call of sisterhood!

I remember after my sixth treatment in September, the boys and I stayed with Jan and her family for almost a week because Ian was out of the country on business. Ben was very poorly at this time, but Jan just matter-of-factly took everyone under her wing, like a mother hen, and cared for us all. I stayed up late one night praying and thanking God for her with tears, and for all she was doing. I told God I could never repay her for her kindness, so I asked God to bless her life richly. I knew that she wanted another baby, so I prayed that God would bless Jan with her heart's desire and give her another child. I don't know why, but I was utterly shocked when Jan and her husband Stu, announced some months later that she was thirteen weeks pregnant! I hadn't even suspected or thought that she could be! What a fantastic answer to prayer, and praise God for his blessings on our lives.

So many other women have stood with me and supported me. My other sister, Louise, has also been a tremendous encouragement to me. Like Jan, she was heartbroken and shocked by my diagnosis but has cared for me, talked to me, listened to me, encouraged me and helped me stay positive. She's been like another cheer leader at the side of the track, urging me to stay focused and keep running to the end of the race. When she gave birth to baby Rosie in August 2010, that was a real blessing for our family. I love babies and it was so therapeutic to visit for cuddles with a newborn, precious bundle, during my treatment! My other niece, Isobel, was starting to crawl and toddle, so having cuddles with her was a little more difficult, but she was so incredibly funny and full of character, that she also brightened my days massively.

My aunty Joy, my mum's sister, visited me often and took me for two of my chemotherapy treatments when Ian was away. I think she knew that I missed my mum greatly during the time of my treatment, and that I felt a deep ache for my mum to be with me on the long journey. Joy is very much like a second mum to me and I was blessed to have her support, kindness and protection. I remember having such a good chat the first time she sat with me during chemo at the hospital, that though the process took hours and hours, time went really quickly. I think we covered every topic under the sun that day! Even when I had to endure the dreaded ice gloves and socks for an hour and a half (to stop my nails falling off) our conversation was a brilliant distraction to me. Being a strong Catholic, Joy and her husband, John, and their family, have lit candles for me, held a mass and prayed regularly for my recovery, which I am really grateful for.

Other friends who live far away have prayed faithfully for me, visited me with meals and done practical jobs like ironing. In particular, Becca and Fran from university have stood by me, prayed for and encouraged me on a regular basis. I often think of the story in the Bible in Exodus chapter 17 when I think about Becca and Fran. Here two friends (well, one was actually a brother), Aaron and Hur, stood alongside Moses during a battle. They stood one on each side of him and lifted up his arms when he became weary; they stood and strengthened him, until the battle was won.

> *'The Amalekites came and attacked the Israelites at Rephidim. Moses said to Joshua, "Choose some of our men and go out to fight the Amalekites. Tomorrow I will stand on top of the hill with the staff of God in my hands."*
>
> *So Joshua fought the Amalekites as Moses had ordered, and Moses, Aaron and Hur went to the top of the hill. As long as Moses held up his hands, the Israelites were winning, but whenever he lowered his hands, the Amalekites were winning. When Moses' hands grew tired, they took a stone and put it under him and he sat on it. Aaron and Hur held his hands up—one on one side, one on the other—so that his hands remained steady till sunset. So Joshua overcame the Amalekite army with the sword.'*
> *Exodus 17 v 8-13*

It is a long and tiring battle to go through cancer treatments, and everybody needs somebody to stand alongside them, strengthen and encourage them through the process. I was really touched once when Becca sent me a card of encouragement. In it she wrote that she had been praying for me and that she wanted to share Proverbs 3 with me. She wrote that instead of the words 'wisdom' and 'understanding', she had used this as a prayer and put in my name. How lovely! I was really touched when I looked up and read the verses in Scripture:

> *'Blessed are those who find wisdom,*

> *those who gain understanding,*
> *for she is more profitable than silver*
> *and yields better returns than gold.*
> *She is more precious than rubies;*
> *nothing you desire can compare with her.*
> *Long life is in her right hand;*
> *in her left hand are riches and honour.*
> *Her ways are pleasant ways,*
> *and all her paths are peace.*
> *She is a tree of life to those who take hold of her;*
> *those who hold her fast will be blessed.'*
> *Proverbs 3 v 13-18*

I feel really humbled to read that passage and think of myself. I especially like the verse about long life! Having such a diagnosis brings inevitable worry about how long or short your life will be, but I keep praying for faith to trust God that he knows the future and I ask that he will give me wisdom and understanding to make the most of every day of my life.

So many other friends and family members have walked alongside me, I could fill this book talking about them. Many have visited, prayed, phoned, sent texts and emails, all showing their concern and support. Close friends from work, Ursula and Ellen, have taken me out for lunch and we have talked endlessly (what do you expect from three Speech Therapists?) and laughed a lot together, which has been a really good tonic. Another close friend, Raynor, has taken the boys out to parks, play centres and amusement parks on a number of occasions in the school holidays. I am so grateful for her kindness, especially as she has three of her own children to entertain! I often felt sad that I couldn't do much with my children, but so glad and grateful that other friends were blessing them. Several other friends and family members - Keith and Jan, and Dave and Lisa in particular - have also taken the boys away for weekends, which was great for Ben and Oliver and allowed me the opportunity to rest without worrying about them. Lisa even took up running in different charity events, to raise money for breast cancer charities. She also got people from her work involved (in a very vigorous training programme too!), and her company even made a huge donation to a breast cancer charity because of Lisa, who had been moved by my experience. I think that's fantastic!

Keeping friendships as normal as possible was really important to me. Throughout my treatment, I often met up for coffee with one of my best friends, Claire, who is a Christian and an absolutely lovely person. Conveniently, Claire was on maternity leave for most of my treatment, so we both had spare time on our hands. What I enjoyed most was how 'normal' our chats were - about our children, husbands (a favoured ground for a few moans!), churches, work, friends, TV and not very much about my illness. I needed times like that just to forget, relax and laugh together as friends. I think having a cancer diagnosis is like having a yappy terrier dog at your feet, just like my father-in-law's somewhat annoying dog, Whisky! Often it jumps up at you and yaps loudly in your face, but how lovely are the times when it lays down, quietly sleeping at your feet, so that you almost forget it is there.

Claire was also supportive because of her medical knowledge as a nurse, but she never thrust any information at me, but just allowed me to ask questions and seek her advice when I needed it. Claire and I can sit and talk for hours and hours. Ian always laughs at us, saying I am much quieter and calmer after I've seen Claire, because I have used up my quota of words for the day and consequently give him some peace! Some research shows women speak 7000-8000 words on average per day whereas men speak approximately a third of this number. Claire and I must easily use up most of our daily word allowance in our coffee mornings. In fact, when I asked Ian about me going on a Christian ladies weekend with Claire, and showing some concern over the cost of it, he said if I was spending the whole weekend with Claire and other ladies - and so would use up a week's quota of words - it would be worth every penny! Very cheeky!

My sister-in-law, Sue, was also a big support to me during this time and the experience has definitely brought us closer. Sue herself had breast cancer in 2005. It was great to have someone close to me who I could ask anything of. Having been through the experience herself, Sue was not only able to give me practical advice about the surgery, exercises afterwards, medication and shopping for post-surgery bras etc., but emotionally, she was able to encourage and support me, because she truly understood. She would often phone me for long chats, and encourage me with how well I was coping. Sue is also one of those super fit people who plays badminton and squash many times a week (she puts me to shame!). Her fitness and level of activity gave me hope, and as well as all the emotional support she gave me, her life and her good health were also a real inspiration to me.

I've talked earlier in the book about the ladies in our church praying for me (the intercessors group), and they were so faithful in their prayers throughout all of my treatment. I felt really overwhelmed in church one Sunday and started crying (the boys sitting either side of me, didn't know whether to laugh or cry with me, but were obviously a little embarrassed to have their mum blubbering at their side!). I wasn't crying because I was sad about my illness or fearful of the future; I was crying because I felt so grateful for the church carrying me like that. I later shared with the church that I felt just like the paralysed man who couldn't get to Jesus himself, so his friends carried him on a mat and lowered him through the roof, so that he was brought right before Jesus' feet, to be healed by him (Mark chapter two). My friend, Ellen, from church, would phone me frequently, pray, text and constantly encourage me, often passing messages of love and support from members of the deaf church, while I was absent. Another friend from church, Sheila, visited me often and we always talked and prayed together. Sheila would often bring a word of encouragement or some verses for me to read, and I always found that her visits lifted my spirits and that her words sank into my heart and mind.

In a strange way, I'm glad that I have had this cancer diagnosis and experience in my life, because it has made me realise how blessed I am to have such lovely and wonderful people around me. It's so easy to take our friends and family for granted, but now I am truly grateful for them all. A little like walking around without my glasses and seeing blurred figures around me, it feels as though I have put on sharply focused lenses and now see clearly all that God has given me, and how richly he has blessed my life.

When I came home from the hospital after my second chemotherapy, there was a parcel waiting for me. It was from my Aunty Chris and contained a beautiful prayer shawl that she had knitted. I was often surprised at how incredibly cold it was to receive chemotherapy. All of the drugs to be pumped through the veins were stored in the fridge, so my arm and whole body would often feel freezing during the actual treatment. It was lovely to come home cold and shivering that day, open my parcel and then wrap myself in the lovely pink shawl. In a card, Chris had written:

'May this shawl light gently round your shoulders
bringing comfort and peace.

Like a snowdrop in January heralding the promise of spring,
May you feel swaddled and strengthened,
Valued and cherished.'
(Words by Janet Bristow)

How lovely. That's exactly how I felt - swaddled, comforted, valued and cherished. I still often put on the shawl (in fact I'm wearing it as I type now, on a cold January day) and it reminds me not only of Chris' kindness in knitting the shawl for me, but also of all the girls who stood by me and wrapped me in strength and comfort. I wrote a little prayer-poem, thanking God for all the girls, and all they had done for me.

Thank you for the Girls, Lord!

Thank you for the girls, Lord
Who've all stood by my side
They've held my hands and strengthened me
Along the bumpy ride.

Thank you for their prayers, Lord
And the kind things that they've done
For all the times they've made me laugh
And brought to me some fun.

Thank you for the chats, Lord
You know us girls can talk
For all those conversations
That helped me on this walk.

Thank you they've been there, Lord
Just waiting in the wings.
Not forcing or cajoling me,
Just seeing what each day brings

Thank you for their patience,
Kind words when I was down.

Looking for ways to help me;
Teaching me not to frown.

Thanks for all the coffees,
Gifts and meals too.
There's nothing like a bit of food
To stop you feeling blue!

Thanks for all their energy
Even though I had none.
Even running races,
So research can go on!

Thank you for the girls, Lord
All their goodness that I see
Won't you bless their lives, Lord
For all they've done for me.
Amen

Chapter Fifteen
Husbands and Wives

Aren't men different to women?! We love to talk; they enjoy peace and quiet. We like to socialise and be with other people (especially other women) - they are often happy by themselves. We need to talk about anything and everything - often they talk very little about how they are feeling or what they are going through. Of course, I am generalising massively, but I can only comment on my experience of the men in my life! I know some men are very chatty - my brother is one of them, but on the whole, they are a different species to us ladies. We communicate differently, we interpret things differently, we think and analyse things differently. Ian and I even see colours differently! How on earth do we cope then in marriages and families?! I'm sure it's by the grace of God and that thing called love!

> *'Above all, love each other deeply because love covers over a multitude of sins.'*
> *1 Peter 4 v 8*

> *'Love is patient, love is kind. It does not envy, it does not boast, it is not proud. It is not rude, it is not self seeking, it is not easily angered, it keeps no record of wrongs. Love does not delight in evil but rejoices with the truth. It always protects, always trusts, always hopes, always perseveres. Love never fails.'*
> *1 Corinthians 13 v 4-8*

I feel so blessed to be married to Ian. Don't misunderstand me. We argue, disagree and fall out, but we love each other deeply. Ian is my best friend, my rock, my strength in the storm, my laughter, my hope for the future and my very breath. After twenty years of marriage, we're no longer two people, but a metamorphosis of two into one.

I often look back and think, what if I'd gone to a different university, or stayed in a different hall of residence - I would never have met Ian and never had Ben and Oliver. Yet God had plans for us to meet, I believe, before either of us chose

Sheffield University. We actually met on the very first day of our attendance there. I'd met a girl, Fran, several times during the rounds of university interviews earlier in the year and so when we found each other in the same hall of residence, on the same course, we became instant friends. I was sitting in the dining room with Fran, eating dinner. Ian had also befriended Graham (later to become his best man) by this time and they spotted this gorgeous girl on the table, gave each other a knowing raise of the eyebrows, and came and sat down. I of course, was sitting next to her! The four of us started chatting and I noticed Ian was wearing an ichthus on his denim jacket (I won't mention the pink jeans which he later became famous for - this was the eighties after all!). I asked if he was a Christian and said I was too, and so we became friends. It all started there - God was weaving the tapestry of our lives already on that first day. It reminds me again of that favoured verse in Jeremiah which God keeps reminding me of:

> *"'For I know the plans I have for you," declares the Lord "plans to prosper you and not to harm you, plans to give you hope and a future."'*
> *Jeremiah 29 v 11*

Needless to say, Ian eventually took his eyes off Fran and we started going out. I knew within weeks that we would get married and this would be the man I would spend the rest of my life with. Two years later, Ian proposed to me in the botanical gardens (very romantic) and much to the horror of our parents, we decided to get married after our third year of study (we were both doing four year courses). Soon after proposing, Ian promptly went to France for a year as part of his course and left me to organise the wedding! Friends and family thought we were mad and that the marriage wouldn't last, but we wanted to honour God and not sleep together or live together first, and we believed God had ordained for us to be together. Over twenty years later we are not only stronger and more mature in terms of our marriage, but we are also closer friends than we have ever been.

Ian stood by me and supported me through my illness, as any committed husband would do, but more than that, I felt as though he too was a victim of the hard card that life had dealt us. He cried with me over my diagnosis, was there waiting at my bed when I woke up from surgery, held my hand through the chemotherapy, and distracted me when I was nearly fainting from being such a whimp over the needles! He let me sleep and rest when I needed to, took charge of the boys, helped with housework, talked to me, laughed with me, prayed with me, comforted and strengthened me. I don't think I could have got through the experience without him.

> *'Two are better than one... If one falls down, his friend can help him up.'*
> *Ecclesiastes 4 v 9-10*

Ian is a lovely man. He is very caring, kind, thoughtful, extremely hard-working, a devoted husband and father, and very clever. He is definitely a perfectionist, and sets very high standards in all that he does: the four year wait for carpet in my new house (while he decorated) certainly gave me a lesson in patience! I love the verse in Song of Solomon, that describes him to me.

> *'He is altogether lovely.'*
> *Song of Songs 5 v 16*

Ian's love for me has been complete, total and unconditional. He has accepted all the changes in my body and loved me just the same. Even though I have felt ugly, he has assured me that I am beautiful in his eyes and this has filled me with confidence. There is another verse in Song of Songs that is true of Ian and that is:

> *'His banner over me is love.'*
> *Song of Songs 2 v 4*

It is as if Ian has held his love publicly over my head, protecting me and declaring his complete acceptance of me, for all to see. If Ian can love and care for me so deeply, then it humbles me to realise how vast God's love and care for me really is. God doesn't just stand by and watch us from a distance when we go through traumas in our lives. He is there, right next to us, holding and uplifting us, like an ever attentive husband. He cries when we cry, mourns when we mourn and rejoices when we rejoice! His love for us is just as intimate and accepting. To take a quote from UCB's 'Word for Today' - 'In tough times, we are more than ever the object of his love and concern.' (Word for Today 8th August 2010). I know God has held my hand, strengthened, comforted and protected me just like a husband does, and he too puts a banner of love over me. There is a song by Kevin Prosch, based on these verses in the Bible:

He brought me to his banqueting table

He brought me to his banqueting table
And his banner over me is love
I am my beloved's and he is mine
I am my beloved's and he is mine

And his banner over me is love
Yes his banner over me is love

We can feel the love of God in this place
We believe your goodness
We receive your grace
We delight ourselves at your table oh God
You do all things well, just look at our lives
And his banner over me is love
Yes his banner over me is love
His banner over you, his banner over me
His banner over us, it is love, love, love

Prosch Kevin © 1991 Mercy/Vineyard Publishing
(admin. by Song Solutions Copycare www.songsolutions.org)

I think emotionally, Ian found my cancer experience and diagnosis, more traumatic than I did. I've seen this before in other relationships - including that of my mum and dad - when my dad was so crushed at my mum's diagnosis and rapid deterioration. My mum stayed incredibly strong, inspiring us all, whereas my dad silently crumbled at her side. I remember when the consultant gave Ian and me the actual diagnosis, I stayed quite calm and asked lots of questions, whereas Ian went white and silent from the shock. In lots of ways, I think it is harder for the spouse or partner than the person with the cancer. I know if it had been the other way round, I would have been devastated to watch Ian suffer and for him to be told he had a life-threatening illness, and I would have just wanted to suffer in his place. I know this is how Ian felt, and he too had to lean heavily on God for comfort and strength in his own sadness.

I talked in an earlier chapter about going through the storm and a period of depression and sadness just after my surgery and before the chemotherapy started. This was also a strange time for Ian and me, and one where I felt particularly distant from him. For several weeks, we struggled to talk and our communication seemed to be drenched in sadness and distance. It was strange in that really when we needed each other most, we almost pushed each other away.

I was recently reading the book by John Gray 'Men are from Mars, Women are from Venus', which I had intended reading for years but never got round to. Although a little old, I have found it really interesting in its descriptions of the relationships between men and women and how we cope differently with conflict and stress. One chapter, the title of which amused me, was 'Men go to their caves and women talk'. The chapter discussed how men instinctively want to solve problems and when a situation arises they withdraw to try and find a solution. Women on the other hand don't want to find a solution but they just want acceptance, to talk about the problem and to be listened to. I think in every other situation in my life, this is true of me. I do love to talk, but for some reason during this particular time in my life, I too went into a cave and became somewhat silent.

It took a few weeks before we sat down together and I had a good cry and told Ian how I honestly felt. I told him about all the negative emotions, worries and thoughts that were going through my head, and that while I realised he was suffering too, I needed him to communicate with me. We talked and prayed together. He shot out of that cave faster than a bolt of lightning at that point and began to hold me more, listen to me more and to support me in an incredible way.

Maybe you are reading this and going through a similar time of awkward communication with your spouse, partner or friend, due to your illness. I would encourage you to accept, hug and listen to each other. There are times we will need to go into caves and withdraw (especially men) and as women I think we need to allow a man that time of grieving. But be honest with each other too. Explain that you need to talk, when you need to talk. Don't keep all your feelings and emotions bottled up - share them. John Gray talks about the need for men to listen and not try to solve problems and for women to know when to talk and when not to - to respect when men need those times to withdraw. A little like keeping a spirit-level, level on a rocking horse - there needs to be balance and support, patience and compassion on both sides.

There is an interesting verse in Song of Solomon about relationships between couples, and something that the man says to the woman:

> *'My dove in the clefts of the rock,*
> *in the hiding places on the mountainside,*
> *show me your face,*
> *let me hear your voice;*
> *for your voice is sweet,*
> *and your face is lovely.*
> *Catch for us the foxes,*
> *the little foxes*
> *that ruin the vineyards,*
> *our vineyards that are in bloom.'*
> *Song of Solomon 2 v 14-15*

Ian would say this was an unusual verse because the man is asking to hear the woman's voice and which sane man would do that?! No seriously, this verse shows the man's acceptance of his wife and desire to see and hear her. It talks about those hidden places - in the cleft of the rock on the mountainside. To me, this means those secret places where your hearts are completely exposed to each other and where you shield and protect one another, from the passing storm. I read the 'Life Application Study Bible' and it has an interesting point to make about verse 15:

> *' "The little foxes" are an example of the kinds of problems that can disturb or destroy a relationship. The lovers wanted anything that could potentially cause problems between them to be removed. It is often the "little foxes" that cause the biggest problems in marriage. These irritations must not be minimised or ignored, but identified so that, together, the couple can deal with them.'*

A Prayer.....
Lord, help us deal with the 'little foxes' that run aggressively over our marriage.

Those negative thoughts and feelings that drive us apart.
The secret hurts we don't share, that fester and grow silently
Forgive us when we are too consumed with our own sadness to
    notice each other's.
Give us the courage to hold each other in the cleft of the rock
To support each other in that secret place.
Help us talk with honesty and openness.
Help us listen with understanding and acceptance.
Help us not to judge or condemn
Give us patience, Lord, open hearts and listening ears
Fill us with your love, your peace, your kindness and compassion
And bind us together, Lord, with the cords of your love, which can
    never be broken
Amen

Chapter 16
How Children Cope

When I wrote earlier about my diagnosis, I talked about how painful it was to tell my two sons, Ben then aged eleven and Oliver, then aged only eight, that I had cancer. They were shocked, worried and upset, especially as they knew my friend Jill who had died from breast cancer the year previously. Part of me wondered whether to tell them at all, but I just thought how can I possibly hide the surgery and treatment from them? Also, I felt that we were a family, a close one at that, and that we needed to go through this together.

I never really felt angry with God about my diagnosis and my own suffering, because I trusted that my life was in God's hands. The only thing that made me angry was watching my children suffer, and seeing them become sad, worried and upset, and this did cause me to cry out to God for them and to ask him, 'Why, Lord?'

I've always believed that my children are a gift from God and that actually, they belong to him and are just mine and Ian's temporarily, to look after and to love for God - as if they are on loan to us.

> *'Children are a heritage from the LORD,*
> *offspring a reward from him.*
> *Like arrows in the hands of a warrior*
> *are children born in one's youth.*
> *Blessed is the man*
> *whose quiver is full of them.'*
> *Psalm 127 v 3-5*

The Lord has really blessed us by giving the boys to us, but actually they are his. One day when I was praying for the boys, that God would strengthen and support them through my treatment, God reminded me of the story of Abraham and Isaac in Genesis 22. This story has always disturbed me in some ways, because God asked Abraham to sacrifice his only son Isaac, as a burnt offering. Abraham had been promised children many years before, but he was actually in his old age when he and Sarah conceived their first child, Isaac (Sarah was

90 and Abraham was 100!), so he was long awaited and very precious. The Bible doesn't say how old Isaac was at this time, but he was clearly old enough to talk and ask questions, and I would imagine he was around six or seven. As he walked with his father to the place of sacrifice, he asked his dad where the lamb was that they were going to sacrifice. I wonder how he felt when his dad began to tie him up, bind him and place him on top of the wood on the altar. I'm sure he would have been screaming, terrified at his father's actions, while tears must have poured down Abraham's face as he obeyed what God had told him to do. I wonder if Abraham believed God would raise Isaac from the dead, after he had killed him. Just as Abraham held up his knife, an angel of the Lord told him to stop. I always feel so relieved when I read that bit!

> *"Abraham! Abraham! Do not lay a hand on the boy," he said. "Do not do anything to him. Now I know that you fear God, because you have not withheld from me your son, your only son."*
> *Genesis 22 v 12*

What a lesson in obedience that was and such a heartfelt test for both Abraham and his son, Isaac. I wonder what they said to each other afterwards - they probably just held each other and cried together for such a long, long time. Even through such an agonising experience, God was working in the lives of both Abraham and Isaac - testing them and preparing them both for a life of service to him.

I felt God was saying to me, that even though I was angry because my boys were suffering, and that it was unjust for them at such a young age to watch their mum go through chemotherapy - he had them in his hands and that they too, were his. He would not let them be harmed or sacrificed in the process. He would not let them be burnt or wounded. Through such a heartfelt experience, such a time of testing and tears, God's will would be done and good would come out of it.

> *'And we know that in all things God works for the good of those who love him, who have been called according to his purpose.'*
> *Romans 8 v 28*

As parents we want to protect our children, keep them safe and free from harm - physical and emotional. Unfortunately the harsh reality is that in today's cruel world, they are not exempt from suffering. I cry out to God to watch over my children and keep them safe all the time. I worry about them crossing roads, playing out, even swimming - I am often the paranoid mother, anxiously waiting for them to come up for air after they have jumped in the pool! But I have to trust God with my children. They too will walk through fires in their lives, just as the prophet Isaiah says:

> *'But now, this is what the LORD says—*
> *he who created you, Jacob,*
> *he who formed you, Israel:*
> *"Do not fear, for I have redeemed you;*
> *I have summoned you by name; you are mine.*
> *When you pass through the waters,*
> *I will be with you;*
> *and when you pass through the rivers,*
> *they will not sweep over you.*
> *When you walk through the fire,*
> *you will not be burned;*
> *the flames will not set you ablaze.*
> *For I am the LORD your God,*
> *the Holy One of Israel, your Saviour.'*
> *Isaiah 43 v 1-3*

Just as God is with us, and alongside us in our sufferings and trials, so he is with our children. They are his precious creation, they belong to him and we have to trust that God has their lives in his hands, that he will protect them and that he has a plan for them - just as much as he has for us. As Ian and I have made him the Lord of our home, we have to accept that he will mould our family, and build our house in his way, not ours, even if this means allowing suffering as part of the moulding process.

> *'Unless the LORD builds the house,*
> *the builders labour in vain.*
> *Unless the LORD watches over the city,*
> *the guards stand watch in vain.'*
> *Psalm 127 v 1-2*

The boys were both incredibly brave during the whole experience. I think they were afraid at times, and spoke to their dad about their secret and hidden fears. Looking back, they were an incredible inspiration to me in so many ways and helped to keep things normal and in proportion. They made me laugh a lot. Ben especially is very witty and has a really dry sense of humour, so he often had me in stitches with the things that he said. I once asked him if he wanted to go for counselling to talk about losing my hair, as another family had done. He said "Nay! (a real Wigan word) If you're alright with being a baldie, so are we!" Oliver is very sensitive and loving and would often just cuddle me for ages, which was lovely.

Both boys have been changed for the better, I believe, because of the experience. Firstly, our love for each other is sharpened and more overt. We have always been a family who tell each other often that we love each other, but both of my boys just tell me at random times and places, every day, that they love me, which really touches my heart. In fact it has even got to the point now where they have realised a very worthwhile strategy. If ever I get angry with them and tell them off, they give me the 'big eyes treatment' a little like Puss in Boots in the Shrek films, and say "Sorry, mum. I love you, mum." My defences are immediately down and anger melted in the moment! A very useful tactic, which we often laugh about!

They are also more compassionate and caring now about other people, more patient and considerate of how other people are feeling and what they are going through. Our time together is much more precious now. When I started to take them swimming again after having not been able to for such a long time, it was great to have fun and laugh together in the water. Ben and Oli also prayed for me faithfully every night of my illness and I believe that they drew closer to God as a result. I have talked openly with them about the words and encouragement that God has given me and about my trust in him. I love the verse in Deuteronomy that talks about sharing your love for God with your children and that is what I have tried to do.

'Love the LORD your God with all your heart and with all your soul and with all your strength. These commandments that I give you today are to be on your hearts. Impress them on your children. Talk about them when you sit at home and when you walk along the road, when you lie

*down and when you get up. Tie them as symbols on your hands and
bind them on your foreheads. Write them on the doorframes of your
houses and on your gates.'*
Deuteronomy 6 v 5-9

I hope and pray that God will have sown seeds in my sons that will prepare them for their futures. I know he has brought good out of the situation for the boys too - and I hope that they will always know his faithfulness and his hand on their lives.

*'Train a child in the way he should go and when he is old he will not
depart from it.'*
Proverbs 22 v 6

To conclude this chapter, I have also asked Ben and Oliver to write a short paragraph about their experience, how God helped them and what advice they would give to other children their age, going through the same experience. So now it's over to the boys:

Oli (aged 10 at time of writing)
I felt sad when mum and dad told me that my mum had breast cancer. I felt sorry for my mum when she told me how painful her operation was. It took me time to get used to all the things that changed about my mum. Losing her hair was quite a shock and she had to go to hospital a lot. However, God made me strong and I slowly got used to everything. I prayed for my mum a lot to get better and I hoped that when it finished she would be as good as new. To other people of my age whose mums have cancer, I would say God will help you and your mum over time. I would tell you it will be alright, just be brave and you should look after your mum. She will need lots of your cuddles.

Ben (aged 12 at time of writing)
When I first found out my mum had cancer I felt really upset and really worried because I was thinking of some possible consequences. I prayed to God every night to help my mum heal and I always asked my mum how she was doing, and no surprise, she seemed to be getting better and better the more I prayed. For any lad my age who is going through the same, it's easier

said than done, but try not to worry. Always remember to support whoever is going through it because they are the ones who need your help the most. And talk about it to your mates, because they are the people who will make you feel better and cheer you up when you need it.

Chapter Seventeen
Losing my Hair and Confidence but Finding a Diamond

When I was a child I had a fairly low self-image, and was quite shy. I remember blushing a lot at school and other children laughing at me and saying "Look at Helen - she's gone red again!" I always felt that my sisters were much more pretty and outgoing than I was. They seemed to have more friends and to get boyfriends more easily than I did. I was a bit more of a quiet 'geek' who enjoyed studying and exams! It was only really when I went to university and met and married Ian, that my self-confidence started to grow. When Ben was born and I became a mum for the first time, I found a new confidence and relished every minute of motherhood. His birth put a spring in my step and a real joy in my heart and I definitely changed as a person at that time. For the first time, I was no longer bothered about what other people thought of me, and I didn't feel inferior.

Having said that, I've never really had a lot of confidence about my body. I've mentioned previously my cellulite-orange-peel legs, but I also have a wobbly jelly belly and rather large bottom. Couple this with thick, wiry, curly hair, glasses and a big nose and now you can see why I've never been very confident! I always remember offending Becca, my friend from university, in the very first few days of our attendance, when I described my hair as "even more wild than yours!" We still laugh about that comment now!

Experiencing cancer treatment and surgery has totally rocked my self-confidence and body image to the core. Like the tall tree battered and torn in the storm, my roots have been tested and only through God's grace and strength, do I still stand. I've already talked about how I felt about losing one of my breasts and that I did not feel like a full or proper woman. I couldn't look at myself for a long time and still wince at times when I catch sight of myself unexpectedly in the mirror. However, one of the most traumatic things for me, was losing my hair.

Again, my friend Jill had been a model for me and she had not been at all bothered about losing her hair as part of chemotherapy, and shaved it all off before her treatment began. I, however, was not so brave and could never quite get to that point of shaving it all off, so I just waited until it fell out of its own accord. I remember that the anticipation of losing my hair was almost worse than actually losing it and I wrote a prayer about how sad I felt about the whole business:

Losing My Hair

Lord, I'm worrying about losing my hair.
I'm dreading the big clumps coming out in my hands (and with the
*   amount and wildness of my hair, they'll be mighty big clumps!)*
I feel afraid, Lord, nervously waiting.
What will I look like when I'm bald?
I feel stripped, naked, bare for all to see, embarrassed to the core.
But your word says 'I consider everything a loss compared to the
*   surpassing greatness of knowing Christ' (Philippians 3 v 8)*
You too were stripped, naked, bare and embarrassed.
Help me to know Christ more deeply through this time and
*   experience*
I pray that your humility, grace and courage would dwell inside me
*   and shine out of me.*
And may my baldie head somehow reflect you.
Amen

When the time came, I had one day's notice as to when my chemotherapy would start. Ideally, I wanted to get my wig before it started in case my hair came out straight away. However, I could only get a wig once I had a voucher from my consultant, who I only saw the day before. Amazingly, the wig shop had one spare appointment for a fitting in the morning of my first chemotherapy treatment session, so I believe that was God's incredible timing.

I was actually quite impressed with the wigs on offer and had a good laugh with Jan, my sister, at the different colours and style of wigs. My hair is naturally a dark blonde/light brown colour and I was going through a phase of straightening it. This took ages and ages, as my hair was so thick, but having had curly hair all my life, I was really enjoying having straight hair for a change. When I found a wig that was a very similar colour to mine, but in a straight 'bob', I was really pleased, as it was the look I had tried to obtain (but never quite managed) with all my hours of straightening! It was lovely, but was nevertheless still a wig, and felt very obviously so. The lady in the wig shop asked which type of chemotherapy I was going to receive and when I said 'epirubicin', she explained that my hair would come out fifteen days after the first treatment. Bizarrely, she was absolutely right. She also told me that I didn't have to shave it, and that I would know when the time came if I needed to shave my head or could cope with it just falling out. This certainly calmed me. She advised me to buy a cotton turban to help catch the hair and this would then be useful to sleep in when I was bald, as my head would get cold at night. This was also very true and I later went to Scotland on holiday and forgot to take my pink sleeping turban, so had to sleep with a pair of knickers on my head! Unfortunately, the leg holes were rather too big for my ears and I realised that my backside is obviously much larger than my head, so the knickers were too big to stay on my head all night! Funny!

A few days before 'day fifteen', I was straightening my hair and when I had finished, I noticed a circle of hairs all around me on the bed. I felt sad that the hair loss had started, but just prayed for peace. Ian was again unfortunately away during this week, so it was something I had to go through largely on my own. Over the next couple of days, my hair continued to thin and then on day fifteen, it started coming out in clumps. I remember washing it and looking at my hands which were totally covered with hairs, and getting upset in the shower. I also remember driving and just stroking my hair, and loads would come out in my hand which I then simply threw out of the window! Every time I touched my head, hairs would pour out and it really was a messy business. The baldness started at the top of my head at the point of my parting, and I remember texting my sisters to say that my parting was now so huge that it was wide enough for the Israelites to cross through, as they had done the Red Sea!

Despite how sad I felt inside at the changes happening to me, I tried to keep things light hearted and even humorous for Ben and Oliver's sake. The boys and I once laughed as I ran a bath for Oliver, but we had to empty it away as it was so full of my hairs, just from leaning over! I told the boys that I felt like a dog shedding hairs everywhere and so needed to hoover constantly. I wrote a poem about the funny side of going bald!

Hairs, hairs everywhere
Over here and over there.

In the bath and in the dinner
Quickly getting thinner and thinner
Stick to my face, putting skin cream on
Increasingly looking like Uncle John
They cover the carpet, stick to my clothes
Fill the dishwasher, drip on my nose.
My boys help me see the funny side
Fill me with love so I don't need to hide
I'm trying to be brave and not to moan
At least it's a way of losing a stone!
I look like the witch out of Robin Hood
But God keeps me going, as only he could!

Over the next couple of weeks, I lost all the hair from my body and one of the hardest things to lose, were my eyelashes. I had quite long eyelashes, and again it got to a point where every time I touched my eyes, more eyelashes would fall down my cheeks until there were none left. I said to my friends that I felt like a plucked Christmas turkey!

When I looked in the mirror, totally bald and without eyelashes and eyebrows, I felt as if I had aged massively. I had to remind myself that I was forty, because the face that stared back at me in the mirror was one I didn't recognise and looked at least twenty years older.

A couple of months after the end of my treatment, I started a new fitness regime and signed up for a healthy living programme at a local gym. I needed to go for a special swimming costume fitting, for ladies like myself who have had a mastectomy, and use a swimming prosthesis. It is embarrassing enough to have to try on swimming costumes in front of a stranger, but as I looked at myself in the unnecessarily huge, full length mirror that day (bald head, one boob, massive scar, fat legs and wobbly belly) I just had to laugh because it was such an awful sight!

But God spoke to me that day and reminded me of something he had been saying to me in his still, quiet voice, and through the words of others, right throughout my treatment, which was that to him, and in my Heavenly Father's eyes, I was beautiful, I was precious, I was his child and it didn't matter what my outward body looked like.

'Therefore we do not lose heart. Though outwardly we are wasting away, yet inwardly we are being renewed day by day. For our light and momentary troubles are achieving for us an eternal glory that far outweighs them all. So we fix our eyes not on what is seen, but on what is unseen, since what is seen is temporary, but what is unseen is eternal.'
2 Corinthians 4 v 16-18

I've already written about the lovely words my then eight year old son said to me after my surgery - "Have you only got one boob now, Mum? It doesn't matter. You're still beautiful and I love you!" Wow - what amazing words from such a young child. My husband and my eldest son have also told me endlessly that I was beautiful, even though I didn't feel it. They loved and accepted me unconditionally. But if my family could look at me, love me and say these wonderful things, then how much more does God look at me, love me and also think I'm beautiful!

'Your beauty should not come from outward adornment, such as elaborate hairstyles and the wearing of gold jewellery or fine clothes. Rather, it should be that of your inner self, the unfading beauty of a gentle and quiet spirit, which is of great worth in God's sight.'
1 Peter 3 v 3-4

It doesn't matter what our earthly bodies look like, because God created us - each one of us - in a divine and unique way. Yes, we should of course look after our bodies and live a healthy lifestyle, but we shouldn't be sad or mourn the fact that we don't look like a film star! We are all part of his masterpiece of design. I remember at university, because I was doing a medical science degree, I had to study anatomy, which involved human dissection. At first I was appalled and disgusted that this was part of the curriculum and I had nightmares about the sights I saw. However, once I had overcome this shock, I stood in awe of God and his creation of the human body. So many intricate, biological systems working together to digest food, process language, create movement - it was truly amazing to study such a magnificent creation and I need to remember that more! Also, one day when we meet God in heaven, we have the promise that we will be given a new body, because of Christ's resurrection. I wonder how amazing a creation that will be!

'So will it be with the resurrection of the dead. The body that is sown is perishable, it is raised imperishable; it is sown in dishonour, it is raised in glory; it is sown in weakness, it is raised in power; it is sown a natural body, it is raised a spiritual body.'
1 Corinthians 15 v 42-44

God always amazes me by his timing of events. I am writing the second half of this chapter, having just returned from a Nancy Goudie Spiritual Health weekend in Preston, northern England. My friend Claire went last year, had a brilliant time and took me along this year. The weekend was called 'You are Special' and was absolutely fantastic! I spoke to Nancy at the end of the conference and asked her permission to write about the weekend in this book, which she kindly gave.

God spoke to me in a very deep and personal way throughout the weekend, and so many of the things that Nancy said in her talks, God had already said to me throughout the previous ten months. Many of them, I have already written in this book. I seemed to spend the whole weekend crying as I realised how deeply God loved me! Some of the things God said included... you are precious; you are beautiful; you are my bride; you are my creation; you are my child; I love you. His love is like a waterfall that pours over us, saturates and soaks us, deep into our hearts.

I love the following quote 'Do you know?' from Nancy's book 'You are Special,' which I bought at the weekend. In this passage, she combines many beautiful Scriptures to portray the adoring love we have from our Father God, and how unique we are in his eyes.

Do you know?

Do you know you are more precious than silver and more valuable than gold? Do you know that I created you in the secret place and formed you in the womb; that I crafted you with love and moulded you with grace? Do you know I chose you to be mine before the world was created? Do you know I made plans for you, plans to prosper you and not to harm you, plans to give you hope and a future?
Do you know?
Do you know that from the beginning I have lovingly carried you in

my arms? Do you know that my loving gaze is upon you and that my fragrance is poured over you? Do you know that every day I place my kiss upon your soul and I hug you to myself? Do you know that I have willingly given all for you and I would do it all again!
Do you know? Do you know?
©You are Special by Nancy Goudie
Printed with permission from the author

Some verses that encouraged me over the weekend were:

'See what great love the Father has lavished on us, that we should be called children of God! And that is what we are!'
1 John 3 v 1

'Can a mother forget the baby at her breast
  and have no compassion on the child she has borne?
Though she may forget, I will not forget you!
See, I have engraved you on the palms of my hands.'
Isaiah 49 v 15

On the Saturday morning, Nancy talked about us being a diamond in God's eyes. I had a very clear picture as we sang beautiful worship songs and it was of a huge diamond on a rotating stand, glistening and turning slowly. I felt God say to me, your name 'Helen', means light and you have tried to be a light throughout your illness, but actually you are my diamond, and that is how my light is reflected from you in so many different directions. Then as I closed my eyes and watched the diamond turn, it became me! I was physically standing there on the rotating stand for a brief moment, and then it changed back to a diamond! Tears were streaming down my face, as I realised how precious I was to God and what I really meant to him.

Nancy later gave us all a cupcake to meditate on. I've never really done any Christian meditation before and in all honesty I wondered what on earth she was giving us a cupcake for! That's bizarre! However, as the cakes were handed round, they looked delicious, had sparkly icing on top and an edible diamond on them. Nancy said she wanted us to think about being a diamond in God's eyes and to eat the diamond (then or later) so that it was physically inside us.

I decided to save my cake for later and eat it prayerfully on my own. I took it to my room and as I ate some lunch, I put on the television. As I sat down to watch it, I realised the programme was about cancer and a 45 year old man dying. I immediately thought - 'Oh no, I can't get away from this' and went to turn the TV off. Just then, the man's wife and children came onto the programme and their grief and suffering was so incredibly sad to watch. I turned off the TV and quietly ate my cupcake. I saved the diamond until last and as I ate and crunched it, I suddenly thought - Oh no, the diamond is crushed and broken! Just then, at that exact minute, I felt God say to me, you have been crushed and broken too, but now there are many diamonds on that rotating stand, all sparkling and reflecting my light even more than before. I closed my eyes and saw again that rotating stand, now covered in broken, crushed diamonds; but this time, hands came slowly, one by one, and took a diamond away from the rotating stand. I felt God say that because of my experience and my own brokenness, I now needed to share his grace, compassion and love with other cancer patients and their families, just like the ones I had seen on the programme. What a commission!

I later shared this with a couple of ladies from Nancy's team, and asked them to pray for me. They both prayed (on separate occasions) and thanked God that light shone from my radiant face! One lady, Kate, said she could see me ministering in hospitals and homes, visiting the sick and them being glad to see me because of the joy and peace I would bring. How amazing! She also said that many would come to know God because of me, and I sincerely hope and pray that all that happens! Praise God!

Another thing that happened after I received prayer, was that a young girl on the conference (she looked about 12) came up to me and gave me a little card that she had made and coloured. On one side it said 'Shine from the inside out' and on the other side it said 'You are special'. How incredible that God could use a child to confirm his word to me!

One thing that really touched me was going through a chain of encouragement and receiving an individual card from Nancy. She and her team had prayed and fasted for all 200 ladies prior to the conference, and Nancy had written down a word from the Lord for each one of us. I half expected something about diamonds or light but instead, it was about beauty in the darkness. I cried again (so many tears!!) as a lady read it to me because I had never really believed in my heart that I was beautiful - especially over the last months of treatment.

Here are a couple of the lines that Nancy wrote for me:

'You are indeed very special; a woman of great beauty and grace! You fill the air with a fragrance so pure and so strong. You delight my eyes and my heart rejoices in you. Can my love reach the depths of life? Yes my love penetrates even the deepest and darkest places. Come, my beautiful Helen. Come, let's dance the dance of life together.'

What incredibly beautiful and amazing words! I feel so blessed to have received them and had them spoken over me. As I went through the chain of encouragement, two other people spoke exactly the same words to me - 'You're flawless and beautiful from head to toe!' Maybe I needed to hear the same words a few times before I believed them.

Maybe you are reading this and feeling exactly how I did - ugly, fat, old, abhorrent even - anything but beautiful. God didn't just say those words to me that weekend. He says them to each and every one of his children - you also are precious. You also are beautiful. You also are his sparkling diamond; his unique and beautiful creation. It doesn't matter what you look like on the outside - God loves you completely and utterly and you are his child. He wants to shine his light on your life and for you to draw near to him. He wants to know you in a deeper way and for you to know how incredibly precious you are to him, and how much he loves you. You are indeed special - special beyond words.

I want to finish this chapter with the words of a beautiful song written especially for the Spiritual Health weekend. The words and music were written by Nancy's husband, Ray, and sung by an incredibly gifted singer, Esther Howgill. This was almost the 'theme tune' of the weekend and is called 'Special One'. God sings this to us and over us - how great is his love!

Special One

You're absolutely flawless
You're beautiful to me
A diamond like no other
That sparkles endlessly
Your beauty shines from head to toe
And sets my heart alight

I'm with you every morning
And hold you through the night

Oh special one, my special one
Don't turn your face away
Oh special one, my special one
I love you - hear me say
I love you more than precious gold
Such beauty to behold
Oh special one. My special one - is you

Don't hide amongst the shadows
Step out of loneliness
Come feel your arms around me
And feel my tenderness
Your name excites my holy passion
And fills me with delight
Your kisses are like honey
My bride all dressed in white

Oh special one, my special one
Don't turn your face away
Oh special one, my special one
I love you - hear me say
I love you more than precious gold
Such beauty to behold
Oh special one. My special one - is you

Ray Goudie/Phil Barlow 2011
(Printed with permission from NGM Publishing/
Integrity Music Europe)

Chapter Eighteen
Fix your eyes

As I was going through the seemingly endless months of chemotherapy, it felt as if time was standing still. Do you know the feeling when you are having a fabulous time and hours feel like minutes - they pass so quickly? The opposite is true going through cancer treatment, and for me it felt as if I would never reach my final treatment date and get healthy again. I'd never really been used to having so much time on my hands before. I live a really busy life - working three or four days a week, running a home, looking after the children, being the taxi service for my children's social and sporting activities, signing and deaf ministries at church, being mum and dad when Ian is away etc. At first, all the free time was a real novelty and I loved the opportunity to read, relax and watch TV. Of course, I read many speech therapy journals and watched intellectual documentaries - not! No, I enjoyed mind-numbing television and sank to the depths of Jeremy Kyle and Bargain Hunt, as well as reading comedy romances and 'chick-lit'. Facing something so serious and life-threatening, made me in need of some light-hearted distraction! In the weeks after my surgery, my dad would come every day and faithfully make my dinner and we would sit together watching Bargain Hunt! It became part of the routine!

After a while, the novelty of having a lot of free time wore off, and instead I became bored and started to dwell on myself. The free time allowed me to think about how unlucky I was, at only forty, to have this diagnosis and to feel sorry for myself for the treatment and side effects I was experiencing.

Sometimes though, I would watch something on television that would shock me into realising that so many other people in the world, were worse off than me. I once saw a news programme about a teenage girl with cancer, who had lost her hair through chemotherapy. Her twin sister had run various races raising money for children's cancer charities. As I watched them on the news report, I felt ashamed that I had felt so sorry for myself, when they were only around seventeen. I remembered many of the sick children I had worked with during the years of being a Speech Therapist and all the heartbreak that their parents had gone through. I remembered friends who were ill and bereaved, including a friend of Ben's who recently lost his dad at only 42. There is so much suffering and heartbreak in the world. As I remembered all these stories of people around me, I turned them into prayers. I prayed for those girls on the news report, I prayed for children with cancer and their parents, I prayed for sick and bereaved people that I knew, I prayed for Ben's friend. I prayed that God would minister his healing, comfort and peace. It did me good to pray and take my eyes off myself and onto other people.

Over time, I felt God say to me that I had to guard my thoughts and keep my eyes fixed on him, not on myself. As I've mentioned before, this whole experience is like running a race, or rather a marathon - there are many twists and turns, some uphill struggles, rough and smooth paths to tread, but I felt God say I needed to keep my eyes fixed on the finishing line.

> *'For we fix our eyes not on what is seen, but what is unseen. For what is seen is temporary and what is unseen is eternal.'*
> *2 Corinthians 4 v 1*

> *'Therefore, since we are surrounded by such a great cloud of witnesses, let us throw off everything that hinders and the sin that so easily entangles. And let us run with perseverance the race marked out for us, fixing our eyes on Jesus, the pioneer and perfecter of faith. For the joy set before him he endured the cross, scorning its shame, and sat down at the right hand of the throne of God. Consider him who endured such opposition from sinners, so that you will not grow weary and lose heart.'*
> *Hebrews 12 v 1-3*

Consider him - consider Jesus - that is what stands out in that passage for me. It's so easy to forget that Jesus Christ suffered terribly. He was God's precious and perfect only son, but he was cruelly tortured and violently killed for our sin, and he died in our place. God created mankind to be in a perfect relationship with him, but because we sinned and did wrong, that relationship was broken and sin separated us all from God. A little like an adulterous fling ruining a beautiful marriage, the relationship was broken by Adam and Eve's wrongdoing in the garden of Eden, and sin entered the world. The Bible says that the punishment for sin is death:

'For the wages of sin is death, but the gift of God is eternal life in Christ Jesus our Lord.'
Romans 6 v 23

In today's society, the law demands that people are accountable for their actions and that they should be punished when wrongs are committed. In the same way, the sin that we commit makes us accountable to God and worthy of punishment and death. Sin means any wrong that we do against God or each other. A definition in the Collins English dictionary states:

'Sin: Any offence against a principle or standard.'

The truth is that we all sin. Big and small errors - murders, theft, lying, cheating, stealing, deceiving, jealousy - are all transgressions in God's eyes and as a result we deserve to be separated from him when we die. However, just like that wronged husband or wife whose partner broke the relationship because of their actions, God longed to give us another chance at being restored to him. His unending love carried on. His faithfulness and adoration continued. This second chance was in the form of Jesus. He chose to pay the price of our sin and wrongdoing, to take the punishment that we deserve for the wrong we have done and to die in our place. How incredible. There is an amazing passage in the Bible, that describes Jesus' death and suffering. What is amazing about it, is that it was actually written around 680 years before Jesus was even born!

'He had no beauty or majesty to attract us to him,
nothing in his appearance that we should desire him.
He was despised and rejected by mankind,
a man of suffering, and familiar with pain.
Like one from whom people hide their faces
he was despised, and we held him in low esteem.
Surely he took up our pain
and bore our suffering,
yet we considered him punished by God,
stricken by him, and afflicted.
But he was pierced for our transgressions,

he was crushed for our iniquities;
the punishment that brought us peace was on him,
   and by his wounds we are healed.
We all, like sheep, have gone astray,
   each of us has turned to our own way;
and the LORD has laid on him
   the iniquity of us all.
He was oppressed and afflicted,
   yet he did not open his mouth;
he was led like a lamb to the slaughter,
   and as a sheep before its shearers is silent,
   so he did not open his mouth.
By oppression and judgment he was taken away.
   Yet who of his generation protested?
For he was cut off from the land of the living'
Isaiah 53 v 2-8

I love the film 'Armageddon' with Bruce Willis. If you don't know the film, it's about a group of men working on an oil rig, who are specialists at drilling deep into the ocean. When a meteorite is on a collision course with earth, NASA hires them and flies them onto the meteorite to drill a hole deep enough for a nuclear bomb to be planted. This would then destroy the meteorite and save the earth and all the people on it. At the end of the film there is a problem with the detonator for the nuclear device, so one of the men has to stay behind to set it off. They draw straws and Bruce's soon to be son-in-law, TJ, has to stay behind. I always have to fight the tears when I watch the scene where Bruce takes him down from the space ship, they say goodbye and at the last minute Bruce damages TJ's space suit, pushes him back inside, and stays himself. He then bravely stands on the terrifying meteorite and lets off the nuclear device, saving his friends, his daughter and all the world, but losing his own life in the process.

Armageddon is a brilliant story, but Jesus did it for real. Jesus chose to stay behind, to suffer and die to save us. This means that if we choose to believe in him, not only can we know him in a real and personal way now in our everyday lives but when we die, we have the promise that our relationship with God will be restored and we will spend eternity with him:

'For God so loved the world that he gave his one and only Son, that whoever believes in him shall not perish but have eternal life.'
John 3 v 16

You might be reading this and wondering what all this has got to do with breast cancer. The fact is that Jesus suffered. He personally knew and experienced pain, anguish, worry, physical agony, stress, hurt and loneliness, as well as the betrayal and desertion of his friends. The night before his death, in the garden of Gethsemane, Jesus was so stressed out and worried about the suffering that lay ahead of him, that he actually sweated drops of blood. I didn't realise, but this is an actual medical condition called 'haematidrosis'. I watched the film Mel Gibson directed - 'The Passion of the Christ' - a few years ago. I have only ever been able to watch it once as I sobbed so loudly in the cinema as I watched Jesus being whipped repeatedly until his back was utterly torn to shreds. I breathed a sigh of relief when the whipping had finished, and then to my horror, the soldiers turned him over to repeat the whipping on his front. I'll never forget that image and the extent of Jesus' suffering for us. My husband, Ian, wrote a book a few years ago called 'Time to Jump' and in it he wrote about Jesus' death and suffering:

'So having been betrayed, denied, lied against, unfairly condemned, punched, scorned, slapped, spat on, whipped to within an inch of his life, sentenced to a death he did not deserve, had thorns sunk into his skull, beaten again, mocked again, spat on again, and forced to carry a heavy beam of wood a few hundred yards, knowing what was going to happen to him when he got there, the worst was still to come.'

The amazing thing is that Jesus knows our suffering too. He has been there himself and he knows and understands every single emotion we feel, because he has felt them all too. He isn't a distant spiritual being who we hope listens when we pray. He is real, alive and has lived on this earth, in human form. He knows what it is like to experience pain, heartbreak, anxiety, despair and all the fearful emotions that go with suffering. That is why he walks with us, alongside us, taking every step of the journey with us, holding our hands. Do you know that Jesus himself prays for you?

'Christ Jesus who died—more than that, who was raised to life—is at the right hand of God and is also interceding for us.' Romans 8 v 34

Jesus prayed for his disciples and future believers:

'My prayer is not for them alone. I pray also for those who will believe in me through their message.'
John 17 v 20

Do you know that his heart breaks when yours does? Do you know that he wraps his arms around you and cries with you? Do you know the extent of his love for you, in your suffering and at all times?

The story of Jesus isn't only about his life, teaching and death on the cross. It is also about something amazing and incredible, and that is the fact that he rose again, three days after his death, as he told the disciples he would. Jesus' story continues with his resurrection. It advances with hope. It moves forward with joy. It brings the promise of resurrection for us.

We all know the Easter story, but how sad that Easter has become a celebration of eggs and chocolate and the real story of life and new birth is often forgotten. My favourite version of the resurrection story is in John chapter 20, when Jesus appears to Mary Magdalene. Two disciples and Mary went to Jesus' tomb early on the Sunday morning and found it empty and the grave clothes folded neatly where Jesus' body had been. I love that bit - it's as if Jesus folded them saying, "I don't need those any more, thank you very much!"

'Now Mary stood outside the tomb crying. As she wept, she bent over to look into the tomb and saw two angels in white, seated where Jesus' body had been, one at the head and the other at the foot.
They asked her, "Woman, why are you crying?"
"They have taken my Lord away," she said, "and I don't know where they have put him." At this, she turned around and saw Jesus standing there, but she did not realize that it was Jesus.
He asked her, "Woman, why are you crying? Who is it you are looking for?"
Thinking he was the gardener, she said, "Sir, if you have carried him

away, tell me where you have put him, and I will get him."
Jesus said to her, "Mary."
    She turned toward him and cried out in Aramaic, "Rabboni!" (which
means "Teacher").
John 20 v 11-16

Mary didn't see or recognise Jesus, because she was consumed by her pain and her eyes were so full of tears. It is so easy for us to feel the same when we are going through cancer or suffering in our own lives. Our tears blind us; our sorrow confuses us; our sad thoughts overwhelm us. But Jesus is right there - with us and alongside us. The beautiful, risen Christ. He stands at the door of our lives and our suffering - and he says our name. He calls us and he knows us.

> *'Here I am! I stand at the door and knock. If anyone hears my voice and*
> *opens the door, I will come in and eat with that person, and they with me.'*
> *Revelation 3 v 20*

So what about you? Jesus is there knocking on the door of your life. Whether you are suffering or not, whether you are going through cancer or not. Jesus knows your name. He knows your suffering and he longs to share your life with you. He longs to live every day with you, and to hold your hand. He is the faithful husband who will be with you through sickness and through health - for better or for worse. Will you answer the door to your life and let him in?

A Prayer
Father, forgive me
...for the wrongs I've done in my life.
...for the times I've failed you - in my thoughts, words and actions
...for feeling sorry for myself.
Lord, I hear you knocking and I ask you to come into my life and
    live in me and with me.
I know you died to save me and I thank you for your sacrifice and
    suffering.
Thank you for offering me eternal life if I believe in you. I believe,
    Lord.

Come and live every day with me. Let us run the race together.
May my eyes be firmly fixed on you, Lord Jesus - now and forever.
Amen

Chapter Nineteen
The Love of the Father

My dad is a truly wonderful man. He would do anything for any of his children or grandchildren. Since my mum's death nine years ago, he has embraced many of her roles too. He now regularly cooks a roast dinner for ten of us, having never cooked anything really while my mum was alive! He regularly minds my boys and nieces and nephew, often picking them up from school or nursery while we are at work. Since my mum's death he has become skilled in many tasks such as ironing, cleaning, cooking and even changing nappies! As well as this, he spends hours every week (including regular night shifts) doing voluntary work at Samaritans - manning the phones, replying to emails, dealing with heartbreak and training up new volunteers. He has always had a strong, quiet faith and was an elder in our church for a long time. My mum's illness and death broke my dad's heart, as it did with all of us. But through the tragedy, he too has drawn closer to God. My dad reads his Bible and 'Word for Today' every day and he often lends me Christian books he has bought or read himself. My dad's life reminds me of the quote attributed to St Francis of Assisi:

'Preach the gospel at all times and if necessary, use words'

When I was diagnosed with cancer, I felt incredibly guilty about the sadness my diagnosis caused to everyone - but especially to my dad. He had been through this experience only eight years earlier, and had lost his absolute soul mate to the disease, when she was only 56 years of age. I'll always remember crying in my dad's arms on the day of my diagnosis, and seeing him cry too. It reminds me of a similar time when we were very upset together, when I was only about eight years old. My dad came home from hospital and broke the tragic news that my mum had had a still birth and that Jan and I were not going to have a new baby sister after all. The three of us hugging and crying together, is still a very strong memory. But even from the very first day of my diagnosis, my dad held and encouraged me, and said we would get through it and cope together as a family. That is exactly what we did.

My dad, with his usual servant heart came every day after my operation, making me dinner, hoovering, shopping and doing little jobs for me. When I had chemotherapy, he would collect and care for the boys to allow time for me to rest and sleep. He even cooked many of his famous apple or rhubarb pies. He would often come to my house and we would just sit quietly together, watching TV or reading. He was always there when I needed him, ready to help in any way. What a blessing he is to my life and to our family. I wholeheartedly thank God for making him my dad and for all his love and incredible care! His strength, kindness and compassion have been a total inspiration to me and I know I can never repay him for all he has done, so I just pray that God will greatly bless his life!

When I think about my dad's great love for me, when I remember his kindness and generosity, his servant nature, his graciousness and his protection, it makes me realise how deep my heavenly father's love for me must be. When I can look at my own dad and feel so surrounded and protected by his love and care for me, how much more does my heavenly father think the same? Jesus compared our earthly father's love to our heavenly father's:

'Which of you, if your son asks for bread, will give him a stone? Or if he asks for a fish, will give him a snake? If you, then, though you are evil, know how to give good gifts to your children, how much more will your Father in heaven give good gifts to those who ask him!'
Matthew 7 v 9-11

I started this book talking about the time I was celebrating my 40th birthday and I felt so incredibly blessed by God and how my heavenly father had poured blessings into my life. The strange thing is that through this dark and often desperate period in my life, those blessings and good gifts have continued. So often I have felt the father give me his gifts of strength, peace, comfort, friendship, encouragement and courage. I feel as if I have walked more closely with him than ever before and tuned into his voice more carefully, like finding a clear radio signal on a desert island. God is so good and he delights to pour good gifts on his children through the easy, as well as the difficult times.

Being a good father isn't only about giving good gifts of course. It's about an overwhelmingly strong spirit of fatherhood, a fierce protection and authority, coupled with an unyielding love that nurtures, guides, moulds and provides for the child.

I remember when both of our boys were born, Ian and I were totally mesmerised by the sight of them. Such miniscule hands and feet, with tiny nails and eyelashes - to us they were perfect in every way. I can just picture Ian now, lying down on the settee, just watching Ben for hours - only taking his eyes off him to watch football! Ben was born during the 1998 World Cup and if he had been born on time, I know I would have been huffing and puffing on my own in the delivery suite, as England were playing Tunisia. Luckily Ben arrived early and he actually watched his first World Cup match in his dad's arms, when he was only two days old!

I know so many brilliant dads in my life, and my brothers-in-law are among the best examples. Stuart, Jan's husband, is a successful businessman who would do anything for his children. He goes from managing a large team to playing Star Wars, from training headteachers to reading Winnie the Pooh. He marries authority with a calm gentleness and desire to constantly bless and serve his children. Paul (Ian's sister's husband) is a model father with his grown up sons - fostering their independence and growth as people, yet supporting them always. He combines friendship with his unique sense of humour. Ian's brother Keith is another example of a brilliant dad. Keith glows with utter pride over his children - every achievement and milestone is a celebration. He is a strong and fierce protector and I don't envy my niece Ashleigh when she brings home her first boyfriend - the poor lad will be well and truly tested and cross-examined!

All the best and wonderful characteristics we can see in these earthly fathers - all the provision, gentleness, time, kindness, guidance, wisdom and doting love - are so small when we compare them to the awesome love of our father God. I am not saying at all that these fathers do not love enough or serve their children enough - far from it. But when we compare our human love to God the Father's love, it is like looking at ants and elephants.

I love the story of the prodigal son in Luke chapter 15. The younger son asks for half of his father's wealth and promptly squanders it. After much soul-searching and desperation, the son plucks up the courage to return to his father, who welcomes him back with open arms. I remember when Ben came home from school when he was in the reception class (aged five), having written his own version of this story. It still tickles me today because his work, on a huge piece of A3 paper, contained a picture of the son and one sentence "The son went away then came back again." What a brilliant synopsis! What I love about this story is how the father was actually watching and waiting for his son to return. He wasn't busy ploughing fields or counting his money. He wasn't doing something important, annoyed and angry, trying to forget his son. Instead his heart was aching and overflowing with love and longing for his precious child. He didn't forget him, but he watched hopefully and expectantly from a distance, waiting for his return:

> *'But while he was still a long way off, his father saw him and was filled with compassion for him; he ran to his son, threw his arms around him and kissed him. The son said to him, "Father, I have sinned against heaven and against you. I am no longer worthy to be called your son." But the father said to his servants, "Quick! Bring the best robe and put it on him. Put a ring on his finger and sandals on his feet. Bring the fattened calf and kill it. Let's have a feast and celebrate. For this son of mine was dead and is alive again; he was lost and is found." So they began to celebrate.'*
> *Luke 15 v 20-24*

Maybe you have drifted from your heavenly father. Maybe you have never even realised that you have a heavenly father. But the truth is that God is your heavenly father who created you, in a unique and amazing way. He stands and watches you from a distance. He aches to hold you and to be restored to you. He longs for you to come home. My experience of cancer sent me running into my father's arms and I felt his firm embrace the whole time. Don't wait until your world is rocked for you decide to go and seek him. Don't wait until you are so desperate and lost that you have nowhere else to go. Go to him now. He longs to embrace and hold you too. He longs to call you his child.

When I read the gospels I am often really struck by the deep and personal relationship between Jesus and God the Father. So many times Jesus refers to the Father's will and being sent by the Father. In John 17 v 10-11 Jesus prays for himself, the disciples and future believers, time and time again using the word 'Father' and talking about their special relationship.

> *'All I have is yours, and all you have is mine.*
> *Holy Father, protect them by the power of your name, the name you gave me, so that they may be one as we are one.'*

The story of the crucifixion is the ultimate example of Jesus, the Son's submission to the Father's will. Of course he didn't want to suffer and die an agonising death on the cross, but he submitted to the Father's will because he trusted that he knew best.

During my experience of cancer, I too have had to learn to accept and trust that the Father knows best. I don't know why God allows suffering (other than I know it's because of sin in the world), or why he allowed this diagnosis to happen to me. I don't need to know and I don't need to understand - just to accept and believe that my heavenly father is always with me, and that he knows best. Jan told me once that the way I had accepted the cancer, reminded her of a person at a concert who did a 'stage dive'. Being a concert novice, I wasn't really sure what that was, but she explained it was a person who dived off the stage, into the hands of the crowd and was passed around from person to person and then eventually arrived back on the stage. I love that illustration and feel that the reason I could fall flat on my face and stage dive into the crowd, was because I was utterly convinced that the Father's hands were there to catch me.

Another key father figure in my life is my utterly lovely father-in-law, Les. Les is so kind-hearted, funny and protective and one of those people that just melts my heart. I have always had a very close relationship with him. I'll never forget on my wedding day, Les said some of the most beautiful words anyone has ever said to me. I remember getting on the coach, kissing everyone and saying goodbye before they left for Manchester. Les stopped me in the aisle and told me what a great day he had had, and that I had to remember one thing. I can just picture him now with his bright blue eyes and smiley face, saying "Helen, remember, in the Jones family – we don't have 'in-laws', we only have sons and daughters." I was completely accepted and welcomed into the family, and from that moment on, was considered to be 'a true Jones'. We often joke with Paul, my brother-in-law, asking Les why he didn't say that to Paul too, on his wedding day!

Les' love and complete acceptance of me into the family is a real reflection of God's father heart towards us. The Bible talks about us being adopted into his family and that we are God's children, because he fully accepts us as his own. In God's family too, there are no 'in-laws' – only sons and daughters.

'See what great love the Father has lavished on us, that we should be

called children of God! And that is what we are!'
1 John 3 v 1

When I think about the unique relationship and the intimate closeness and trust between Jesus and his heavenly Father, it humbles me to realise that God loves me in the same way. The Bible says that we are co-heirs with Christ; that God adopts us and calls us his very own children:

> *'The Spirit you received brought about your adoption to sonship. And by him we cry, "Abba, Father." The Spirit himself testifies with our spirit that we are God's children. Now if we are children, then we are heirs - heirs of God and co-heirs with Christ.'*
> *Romans 8 v 15-18*

I can't believe I am that precious to God! What an honour; what a privilege, what an incredible gift to be adopted by Jesus' Father - to be called children of God. We are not just brothers or co-heirs of the man next door, of a pop star or even of a famous celebrity. God declares us his very own children and he adopts us into his heavenly family. We are co-heirs with Jesus himself! We are allowed to call him not just 'father' but 'Abba Father' - a term of childlike intimacy. Dr F Wilson in his article 'Names and Titles of God' gives a brilliant definition of the meaning of the word 'abba':

> *'Biblical Hebrew 'ab' is "father." But in Aramaic 'abbä' is a word derived from baby-language. As the Rabbis said, a small child "learns to say 'abbä' (daddy) and 'immä' (mummy).'*

We are so loved, that we can call him 'daddy!' God is a heavenly dad who embraces and protects us; a father who knows us completely but still loves us; a daddy who walks with us through good times and bad; who cherishes us and blesses us with good gifts; a father who offers us the love he shares with his own son, Jesus. A father we can trust at all times and in all situations. A father who I long to be like!

As I write this, I had an interesting experience last night, in the middle of the night. I was looking after my niece and nephew overnight to give my sister a break before the birth of her new baby, in a few weeks' time. Isobel, who (at the time of writing) is 18 months old, woke up crying and wouldn't settle, so I brought her in bed with me and we snuggled together. For the next hour, she sang songs to me. Again and again, she sang beautiful melodies. She stroked my hair, grabbed my cheek if I turned over and climbed on me to get my attention, singing beautiful songs. I couldn't understand much of what she said but it was lovely and touched me deeply, as well as making me laugh a lot!

Isobel's tenderness reminded me that we have a father in heaven who sings over us! His love for us is so great and so immense, and in the deepest, darkest hours of our lives, when we are surrounded by blackness and can't see the way ahead - whether we understand him or not - he sings songs of love to us and over us. What a heavenly father we have!

The Father's Song

I have heard so many songs
Listened to a thousand tongues
But there is one
That sounds above them all

The Father's song
The Father's love
You sung it over me and for eternity
It's written on my heart

Heaven's perfect melody
The Creator's symphony
You are singing over me
The Father's song
Heaven's perfect mystery
The king of love has sent for me
And now you're singing over me
The Father's song

It's Heaven's perfect mystery
The king of love has sent for me

And now you're singing over me
The Father's song

The Father's song
The Father's love
You sung it over me and for eternity
It's written on my heart

Chapter Twenty
'Good as New'

One morning near the end of my treatment, I was walking with Oliver to school and he asked me a question. He seemed a little awkward and looked up at me with those big blue eyes. He said, "Mum, when all your chemo is over, will you be like... good as new?" I suppose in some ways, he had been missing me. I certainly felt as if I could not do as much with my children or look after them the same way that I always had done, and I had to let other people get involved and take over when I was too tired. Oliver's question represented a childlike hope for the future: hope that my illness and treatment would soon be over; hope that the cancer would be gone and we could get back to a normal life. I smiled back at him and said, "Yes sweetheart. I believe I will."

We need to hold onto hope, because an end to our suffering will come. Hebrews 10 v 23 says:

> *'Let us hold unswervingly to the hope we profess, for he who promised is faithful.'*

For me that date was 27th October 2010 - my last chemotherapy treatment. Thankfully, my consultant decided that I didn't need radiotherapy, so my treatment was over sooner than I had expected. What a relief to get to that date and walk out of the hospital that day. What a relief to know that was the final time I would be sick, tired and achey and that soon my body would start to recover.

The night of my last chemotherapy, I was reading the Bible and came across Psalm 23 verse 6:

> *'Surely your goodness and love will follow me all the days of my life.'*

What an incredible promise that is. God's goodness and love will follow me every day, for the rest of my life. Whatever turns and roads my life will take, whatever events or illnesses may lie in my future, I can rest assured knowing that the awesome love of the Father, and his overflowing goodness, will always be with me. As I read that psalm I thought that in a way, God had caused me to lie down beside quiet waters through my illness. It is not a way I would have chosen to lie down or get close to the Lord, but one that I did. Though physically it had been a horrible experience, spiritually I had never felt closer to God, and he certainly had been refreshing my soul.

'The LORD is my shepherd, I lack nothing.
He makes me lie down in green pastures,
he leads me beside quiet waters,
    he refreshes my soul.
He guides me along the right paths
    for his name's sake.
Even though I walk
    through the darkest valley,
I will fear no evil,
    for you are with me;
your rod and your staff,
    they comfort me.
You prepare a table before me
    in the presence of my enemies.
You anoint my head with oil;
    my cup overflows.
Surely your goodness and love will follow me
    all the days of my life,
and I will dwell in the house of the LORD
    forever.'
Psalm 23

It is a shame that we only usually sing or read this psalm at funerals. It contains such comforting and beautiful words. God is indeed a shepherd to us; carefully watching our every move, guiding us, comforting us and protecting us from danger; keeping us from fear and harm. Jesus spoke about being a shepherd in John's gospel:

'I am the good shepherd; I know my sheep and my sheep know me.'
John 10 v 14

They're funny creatures sheep, aren't they? Cute to look at but not very bright and they follow the crowd! In just the same way, we often don't choose God's way, but follow our own paths and those of the people around us. Thankfully Jesus is the good shepherd who watches us and herds us gently back along his paths.

In the weeks after my treatment had ended, I gradually started feeling better and getting my energy back. It was a slow and frustrating process, but over time I felt strong again. I was so excited when my hair and eyebrows started to grow, but one of the best moments was when I noticed my eyelashes were growing again. I often laugh at how many times I would hold and cuddle babies and children and wholeheartedly wish I had eyelashes as long and thick as theirs!

Around this time, my cousin Chloe made me a beautiful green bracelet. She's very creative and clever at craft and things like that. With it she wrote a little card and I was really touched by her gesture and beautiful words:

'A wish for you to be happy and well, sent with love each time I threaded a bead. I chose green, the colour of spring - regeneration - as I thought of you being so strong through a personal 'winter' and then coming out the other side, ready for spring. Made with love for you!'

I returned to work on January 24th 2011 and it felt wonderful to be back again, well enough to work, and seeing my work colleagues and children again. The patient's reactions to my changing hairstyles were funny as I went back in my wig for the first couple of months. One little deaf boy who was six, signed to me - "Mrs Jones. Hair - what's happening? Ages ago curly curly, then straight, straight, now short all gone!"

That first night, after returning to work, as I had my daily prayer time and read my UCB Word for Today, I couldn't believe the verse for the day. It was 1 Peter 5 v 10, the very same verse that God had given me at the time of my diagnosis:

'And the God of all grace, who called you to his eternal glory in Christ, after you have suffered a little while, will himself restore you and make you strong, firm and steadfast.'

It was as if God was reminding me of his faithfulness and of the fulfilment of his promise to me. It was a landmark day - I was back at work. I had been through the suffering and come out the other end. I was physically strong, spiritually firm and emotionally steadfast. His grace had held me throughout the whole agonising process and now he had restored me. What an amazingly faithful God we have! He had indeed walked with me and held my hand through every single step of the cancer journey.

Once I was well again, I started to become aware of the need to stay close to God, but also to improve my health and fitness. I realised that I needed to begin the daunting task of losing weight and following a much healthier diet. My nephew Josh asked me once if I had a baby in my tummy and I replied, "No, it's just too many chocolate muffins!" Several times since, he has come up to me, gently patted my tummy and said "No baby, just too many muffins." How funny!

As part of my plan to begin more exercise, my doctor referred me to our local 'active living team'. I had to attend for a health assessment, and was then put on an exercise programme at a local gym. Being the 'gym-phobic' that I am, it took me two months to act on the doctor's referral, but when I did, I loved it! I ideally had to do my exercise programme two to three times per week and go swimming whenever possible. I've never been interested in gyms before. They have always seemed full of slim, athletic, model-like people who can run for three hours on a treadmill without breaking into a sweat! However, when I went, I found there were lots of ordinary people there, trying to become more healthy, just like me.

After a few weeks, I became even more enthusiastic. I once arrived at the gym and noticed on the timetable that a step class was due to commence in five minutes. It was only for half an hour, and the timetable said it was suitable for beginners. Not being at all confident or sporty, I set up my steps and mat at the very back of the room so I could stay hidden from the aerobic enthusiasts at the front of the class. Unfortunately, I had forgotten that the room was covered in mirrors and that step routines often involve many turns and the group often face different walls, thus embarrassingly placing me at the front of the class and not the back as I had hoped. So much for feeling hidden! By 10.30, fifteen minutes into the class, I was absolutely exhausted - wheezy, aching, sweating and impersonating a cranberry with my bright red face. Only ten minutes to go, I thought - thank goodness! However, 10.45 came and went, as did 10.55

and eventually at 11.05, the class finished. That was one of the hardest fifty minutes of my life! At least I could go home feeling that I had done some good to everyone else's confidence – they must have looked at me and thought at least they weren't as bad as the out-of-time, cellulite-ridden asthmatic on the back row!

I tried to lose weight as part of the process and managed to shed a few pounds, which I promptly put straight back on (and more) when we went on holiday! I've never really been good at losing weight and when I manage to, I just can't keep it off. I have got such a sweet tooth and can't walk past the biscuit or cake tin, without having a nibble. At long last, I decided that I needed to do something serious about losing weight. It wasn't just about getting slim, it was about reducing my chances of a re-occurrence of the disease.

Around this time, I read an article in a cancer magazine that one of the breast care nurses had given me, called 'Amoena Life' (Issue 29). This article was written by Dr Marilyn Glenville, a leading UK nutritionist specialising in women's health, who wrote about how breast cancer treatment can often cause an increase to a lady's weight. This is often due to a combination of the steroids and lower activity levels due to tiredness. What alarmed me was the fact that if breast cancer was oestrogen fuelled, as mine was, and for ladies taking tamoxifen tablets - as I was - the body fights to hold onto fat cells, particularly around a lady's tummy, in order to produce oestrogen. Essentially, the larger my stomach, the bigger the oestrogen-making factory within me that could potentially trigger breast cancer again. How frightening. That was it - I had to get serious about losing weight, and in particular, make every effort to reduce the size of my tummy!

Armed with this new information, I promptly joined Slimming World, a weight loss group in a determined attempt to finally get my weight down once and for all. I can't recommend this highly enough. The people were warm and friendly (certainly very passionate about losing weight) and offered delicious recipes and eating plans. I never thought I was very overweight, but I was shocked to learn that I needed to lose nineteen pounds to reach my target weight. In my first week on the diet, I managed to lose four pounds, so I felt really encouraged. Please don't misunderstand me, it is really tough to lose weight, and I was gutted the following week when I didn't lose anything more. However, I persevered and I have to say there was definitely a fear factor about being weighed every week, that made me accountable! After twelve weeks I was given a very enthusiastic award for losing ten percent of my body weight and more than my intended nineteen pounds. I had dropped a dress size and felt fantastic. I know now that I have to carry on eating, exercising and living this way. I keep praying that God will give me the strength and discipline to continue eating a better diet and looking after my health more.

I want to end this chapter by writing some top tips to get to that point of feeling 'good as new' after chemotherapy and cancer treatment. I've included some physical, spiritual and emotional points, as well as top tips for family and friends. Obviously, this is only from my personal experience and everybody is different, but this is what I have found helpful:

TOP PHYSICAL TIPS
During Treatment:
- Rest when you need to.
- Listen to your body - have a sleep in the day if this helps.
- Ask for help - e.g. with ironing, hoovering, cooking etc.
- Take your medication carefully.
- Do what the hospital advises you to do.
- Never be afraid to ask your medical staff for help or advice.
- Eat well for energy, if you can.
- Treat yourself.
- Join a local support group if this helps.
- Meet often with friends and laugh together.
- Walk regularly. My consultant told me that walking and exercise helps clear the chemicals out of your body faster.
- Keep physically active if you can - try little jobs around the home.
- Try and keep life as normal as you can.
- Keep your mind active - e.g. through reading.
- Talk when you need to talk - don't bottle things up.
- Access internet forums if this helps (see bibliography and references for useful websites).
- Talk to and meet with people who have been through the same. experience. Some churches have a cancer support group – try it.

After Treatment:
- Increase your exercise to build up stamina - try swimming or longer walks.

- Eat well - include a mixture of different coloured fruit and vegetables every day. The health experts say five is the minimum!
- Keep up with future check ups and health screens.
- Monitor yourself and your own body - check your breast/s regularly for lumps. At the end of this book is a guide about how and when to check your breast/s, and what to look out for.
- Continue to take medication carefully.
- Consult your doctor if you have any concerns.
- Try to reach and maintain a healthy weight.
- Sleep well - try to sleep for seven or eight hours each night.
- Be aware of lymphoedema. A few months after the end of my chemotherapy, I developed fluid in my arm from playing squash - even though I had only had three lymph nodes removed. Prevention is much better than cure, so avoid vigorous arm movements and carrying heavy objects. If you do develop it - get a support stocking for your arm and follow exercises from your breast care nurse.

Spiritual and Emotional Tips
- Pray at all times. Talk to God about anything and everything that concerns you - anywhere and at any time.
- Listen to praise music. Even if you don't feel up to praising God, this is a very powerful way to draw close to him and it will lift your mood.
- Read the Bible every day. Try UCB's 'Word for Today' or another Bible reading guide. Read the psalms often, as these express so many emotions which may echo your own feelings and prayers
- Share honestly and openly with close friends and family about how you are feeling and your secret fears and struggles.
- Ask friends to pray with you, as well as for you.
- Text prayer requests to friends according to your specific needs at a particular time e.g. on the day of chemotherapy
- Pray for yourself - it's not wrong to do this!
- Pray for other people. It is good to remember others' needs and sufferings, and not be too absorbed in your own.
- Read Christian books. Fill your mind with good, encouraging thoughts. (Philippians 4 v 8)
- Listen to Christian radio often.

- Watch Christian television and services when you are too ill to get to church.
- Trust God as much as you can. He will walk with you through this long and difficult journey.
- Keep a journal of verses, prayers and other encouragements that people give you. It is often very therapeutic to write, and who knows - your writings may help others in the future.

Top Tips for Friends and Family
- Remember: this is the same person, so treat them in the same way.
- Don't avoid a person because of their diagnosis. They need your friendship now, more than ever.
- Don't be afraid to say that you don't know what to say! Saying this is so much better than saying nothing at all. Often a hug speaks a thousand words.
- Follow the lead of the person with cancer – if they want to talk about their illness, listen. If they don't want to talk about it, respect that and do something else.
- Continue to support your friend throughout the long, slow journey. Everybody sends flowers and cards at the time of the diagnosis, but continue to send cards and messages of love, support and encouragement in the later weeks and months of treatment, too.
- Be aware that the ill person may not want to confide in you for fear of upsetting you. Reassure them that they can tell you anything (if you feel ready to hear anything that is!).
- Offer practical support. Cook meals for the whole family that can be easily reheated or frozen. Do some ironing, hoovering or cleaning. They may not like to ask for help, so just keep offering.
- Take the children out for the day - they are probably missing out on days out or treats, because of their parent's illness.
- Offer lifts to appointments, pick-ups from school or to babysit, so the couple can go out when he/she feels well enough.
- Do some fun things together - meet for coffee, lunch, a few wines etc!
- Laugh often together.
- Pray faithfully for your friend, every day. They really need your prayers!
- Meet together for a specific time of encouragement, maybe 1:1 or 1:2.

Share a worship song, Bible reading and pray together. Ask God to give you specific words of encouragement/pictures/verses to share with your friend.

- Support the spouse. Often they are just as hurt as the person with the diagnosis, and can be easily overlooked. Have some man to man time playing snooker, or a girls' night out etc.
- Text and email often. These are great ways to keep in touch with your friend, when they may not be up to a phonecall.
- Remember their chemotherapy dates - write them on your calendar if you can. Remember to pray especially on that day and support them in practical ways during the next week when they will feel particularly ill.

Chapter Twenty One
Pray at all Times

There is a great verse in 1 Thessalonians 5 (verse 17) that says:

'pray at all times' (Good News version).

In the NIV the same verse (verse 17) is translated as:

'pray continually'.

Throughout this book I have already talked a lot about prayer, and in particular how the prayers of my church held me up and carried me through the trauma of the cancer experience. I am incredibly grateful to all the people who have prayed faithfully for me - friends, family, colleagues - because God has most certainly listened and strengthened me as a result.

I want to talk a little bit more here, about personal prayer. I have to admit that I have never really been good at praying. Often when I sit to have a quiet time, I read the Bible and my notes for the day and then start to pray. I start off focused - thanking God and praying for people and situations. Not long into the prayers, I start thinking about what I'll cook for tea that night, the report that I still haven't finished for that child at work... oops sorry Lord... I get back onto friends who are sick, my nan... I really should go and visit my nan in the home this weekend... I wonder if my sister would like to come as well... oops sorry Lord... I pray for healing in relationships between people I know... I wonder if those friends are speaking yet... I must ring them... Oh no I've drifted again... etc etc. I often wonder if I have got the spiritual version of attention deficit disorder! The Lord must be so frustrated with me at times and must think, Helen will you just stop the distractions and focus on me PLEASE!!!

It is true to say that there is nothing like a life threatening illness to sharpen your prayer life! When your heart is broken and your soul cries out to God, the distractions fade away. Looking back I feel as if my prayer life has been transformed. Not because I have become a mighty spiritual giant who intercedes for the world (which I haven't) but because I have learnt to pray at all times and in every situation.

We don't need to have a set time to pray each day; we don't need to use only prayer books and readings; we don't need to use long sentences and show off our extensive vocabulary. Of course, a set prayer time is fantastic, formal prayers are important and prayer books have their rightful place in our churches - but essentially, I believe we need to pray as if we are talking to our best friend, who walks alongside us, in any and every situation.

Jesus talked about prayer in Matthew chapter 6 verses 6-8:

> *'But when you pray, go into your room, close the door and pray to your Father, who is unseen. Then your Father, who sees what is done in secret, will reward you. And when you pray, do not keep on babbling like pagans, for they think they will be heard because of their many words. Do not be like them, for your Father knows what you need before you ask him.'*

Jesus was talking about the need for simplicity in prayer - saying clearly what it is you want to say. It's an interesting line at the end of the above quote, which says that 'your father knows what you need before you ask him'. How incredible. The fact that the Father already knows our needs, doesn't mean we don't have to pray. Of course we do! I don't have to tell my children that I love them, because they already know - but I am compelled to tell them every day, because I need to speak about what is in my heart. Ian might know that we need milk, but I still need to tell him before he would buy any! (But that is men for you!). We have to communicate openly, honestly, plainly and simply with our father in heaven, as Jesus went on to demonstrate in the Lord's prayer Matthew 6 v 19-22):

> *'This, then, is how you should pray:*
> *'Our Father in heaven,*
> *hallowed be your name,*
> *your kingdom come,*
> *your will be done,*
> *on earth as it is in heaven.*
> *Give us today our daily bread.*
> *And forgive us our debts,*
> *as we also have forgiven our debtors.*

And lead us not into temptation,
but deliver us from the evil one.'

Over the months of my treatment, I have spent times away from everyone, just in prayer. I found that the bath is a brilliant place to pray! But so often I learnt to pray 'on the go'. As I have spent hours in hospital waiting rooms, as needles have been inserted in my body, as I was given the anaesthetic for my operation, as I rested after chemotherapy - I prayed. Often my prayers were so simple and child like - "God help me now... Lord I feel afraid... please give me your strength and make me brave... help me not to faint... keep me going Lord." The Bible says that we should be like children in our faith and I believe sometimes, in our prayers too.

'But Jesus called the children to him and said, "Let the little children
come to me, and do not hinder them, for the kingdom of God belongs to
such as these. Truly I tell you, anyone who will not receive the kingdom
of God like a little child will never enter it.'"Luke 18 v 16-17

As adults we can get 'bogged down' in prayer. It can become a difficult and laborious task. But when we listen to how children pray - their prayers are simple, heartfelt and beautiful and that is how I learnt to pray when I was undergoiong treatment. I also developed a childlike acceptance that God is definitely listening and that he does actually answer.

I remember something that happened several years ago when the boys were little, that showed me so clearly, how powerful prayer is. We were on holiday in Majorca and had spent the early part of the evening at the children's disco, at the site where we were staying. When the disco had finished, Ian took the boys off to the games room while I stayed for the adult show. I hadn't realised before, but the act that night was a hypnotist. I don't know a great deal about hypnotism, but I personally believe it is spiritually wrong in some way and potentially very harmful to those who take part. As soon as the host came on to the stage, I got up to leave, feeling distinctly uneasy. All of a sudden, I was struck by an overwhelming feeling not to run away, but to stay and pray. I remember clearly, sitting quietly and praying fervently that the hypnosis would not work. The man got several people up on the stage and then went round the room selecting volunteers whom he attempted to hypnotise in their seats. What was amazing was that out of the twelve or so people he tried to hypnotise that night, not one of them could be hypnotised. The man was astounded and said he had worked for many years as a hypnotist, and that had never happened before. He didn't know why it hadn't happened that night - but I did. I am absolutely certain that it was because I sat there and prayed against what he was doing.

God listens when we pray. He turns his full and undivided attention to us when he hears our voices. I am ashamed to say that sometimes, when my children talk to me, I only half listen to them. I'm usually busy doing something or other - getting ready for work, making tea, sorting out washing and often Oliver will say to me "Mum, are you actually listening?" That usually shocks me into stopping what I am doing and giving him my full attention. I believe that God not only stops what he is doing to listen, but perhaps heaven even goes quiet when we pray. There is a beautiful picture in the book of Revelation, of heaven going silent and the prayers of the saints rising up to God, like incense:

> 'When he opened the seventh seal, there was silence in heaven for about half an hour. And I saw the seven angels who stand before God, and seven trumpets were given to them. Another angel, who had a golden censer, came and stood at the altar. He was given much incense to offer, with the prayers of all God's people, on the golden altar in front of the throne. The smoke of the incense, together with the prayers of God's people, went up before God from the angel's hand.'
> Revelation 8 v 1-4

How incredible that heaven might stand still when we pray, as our prayers go up to God like a fragrant offering. It makes me ashamed that so many of my prayers are selfish nonsense. One example of this, is that I am always late for everything (I have now given up making new year's resolutions to be on time because they are always broken by 2nd January) and I so often pray - 'Lord, help me to get there on time... help me not to be late'. I often think I can bend time and space to get to one place the same time as I am leaving another! What a waste of a prayer - I just need to get more organised!

Isn't it strange that most people pray when they are going through difficult times - whether they follow God or not? It is as if there is a deep connection inside each one of us that cries out to the Father when we are in need. A deep spiritual umbilical cord, that links our souls to his. And he listens. He listens to every word. He doesn't always answer in the way that we want, but he is God and answers as he chooses.

The Bible also talks about 'praying in the Spirit':

> *'And pray in the Spirit on all occasions with all kinds of prayers and requests. With this in mind, be alert and always keep on praying for all the Lord's people.'*
> *Ephesians 6 v 18*

To me 'praying in the Spirit' means allowing God to direct our prayers; to have his Spirit's influence in who and what we pray for. He often puts things or people on my heart as I am praying and later I have frequently discovered that that particular person has needed my prayers, at that specific time.

When I was thirteen, I went away with the school's Christian Union, camping in Devon. My RE teacher, who led the week, was an evangelical Christian and one night she talked about the Holy Spirit and speaking in tongues. I had never heard of tongues at the time, but we read Acts chapter two about when the Holy Spirit came upon the disciples and they all started speaking in different languages. Many people from many different nations were present and they all heard the good news about Jesus in their own language. That night, in the tent, we prayed for the Holy Spirit to come and asked for the gift of speaking in tongues. From that night, I started to speak in tongues - to form sounds and words in a spiritual language I don't understand. I often now pray in tongues when I don't know what to say in English. I prayed a lot in this way when I was initially diagnosed with cancer and as I faced different stages of the journey. My emotions were often too confused and my words all jumbled, so this was a perfect way to pray. It was as if my spirit was just in communion with God's Spirit and meaningful words weren't needed. I remember the night my mum died, my aunty Joy held me tight as I sobbed my heart out and I suddenly realised that I was praying out loud in tongues, in her arms. I don't know what she thought of that, but that was another example of my own words not being sufficient, as I cried out to God in desperation.

So pray at all times. Use the gift of speaking in tongues if you have it or English if you don't - it doesn't matter which. Whatever illness you face, whatever treatment and recovery you go through, at every appointment, in every waiting room, during all tests and results – pray. Talk openly and honestly to your heavenly father. Yes, he already knows what you need - but he still wants you to ask him and communicate with him. He loves to hear your voice and wants to receive your prayers. You don't have to talk endlessly - the best prayers are often those with the most childlike simplicity. Talk to him as you would to a friend. Remember that heaven could be going quiet when you pray! How awesome is that! So make every word of your prayers count.

Chapter Twenty Two
Seize the Day and Don't Fear the Future

I've always loved the rather tragic film 'Dead Poets Society' and how inspirational a teacher Robin Williams portrayed. He taught the students the Latin words *'carpe diem'* – seize the day. What a fantastic phrase. It means make the most of now, live life to the full, take every opportunity. We don't know what the future holds, so live well today. I recently bought my sisters a bracelet inscribed with the phrase: 'Live well... love much... laugh often.' What a great motto that is too.

I don't know what may or may not happen in my future. I know in my heart that there is a possibility that the cancer may return one day, but with God's help I am refusing to live in fear of that day or to worry about it. At times I do feel gripped with hidden fears, often not sharing those secret worries with anyone other than my heavenly father, but when I do, I again feel him take hold of my hand, strengthen and comfort me. He knows my every thought, my every worry, my every concern, and he loves me completely. God doesn't promise that bad things won't happen to us just because we love and follow him. We are in the world and exposed to everything that the world throws at us, just the same as everyone else. The difference is that he promises to be with us, to walk alongside us, through the waves and the fire of every circumstance.

There is a wonderful line in that great hymn, 'Be thou My Vision':

'Great heart of my own heart, whatever befall,
still be thou my vision, O Ruler of all.'
Translated by Mary Byrne, 1905

I know God has been so faithful to me and walked with me through this cancer experience. Although I don't want it to ever happen again, I know it might; but I trust and know in my heart that God will be with me again. Whatever happens in my future, I want him to remain unswervingly as my life's vision, my hope and my security. His perfect love casts out and abolishes fear inside me and I do not need to be afraid:

> 'There is no fear in love. But perfect love drives out fear.'
> 1 John 4 v 18

This is not to say that I am some kind of super woman who never thinks about it or worries - of course I do. I often get back and neck ache and find myself worrying if the cancer could have come back and be the cause of the aches. I sometimes think about how many years of life I have got left before it may return, and I worry about how old my children will be then. But I just pray. I take all my worries and fears, and give them to God. There is a great passage in Matthew, chapter six where Jesus talks about worry:

> *"Therefore I tell you, do not worry about your life, what you will eat or drink; or about your body, what you will wear. Is not life more than food, and the body more than clothes? Look at the birds of the air; they do not sow or reap or store away in barns, and yet your heavenly Father feeds them. Are you not much more valuable than they? Can any one of you by worrying add a single hour to your life?*
> *"And why do you worry about clothes? See how the flowers of the field grow. They do not labour or spin. Yet I tell you that not even Solomon in all his splendour was dressed like one of these. If that is how God clothes the grass of the field, which is here today and tomorrow is thrown into the fire, will he not much more clothe you—you of little faith? So do not worry, saying, 'What shall we eat?' or 'What shall we drink?' or 'What shall we wear?' For the pagans run after all these things, and your heavenly Father knows that you need them. But seek first his kingdom and his righteousness, and all these things will be given to you as well. Therefore do not worry about tomorrow, for tomorrow will worry about itself. Each day has enough trouble of its own."*

I know that I do not have to be afraid, and I try not to worry. My heavenly father knows what I need - now and always. I know that I must live for now, for today, to seize this very day and enjoy every moment of my life. I want to enjoy every precious minute with my boys, with Ian, with my family and friends.

I recently read a story in the Bible that I had never read before, again as part of my daily readings with UCB's Word for Today (March 7th 2011). The verse for the day was from 2 Kings 7, and the passage told the story of four men with leprosy. As I'm sure you know, leprosy is a horrible, skin wasting disease which attacks the nerves and causes body parts to become numb and diseased. It is an infectious condition and in Biblical times, the law stated that lepers were to be banished outside the city (Numbers 5 v 1-4). Exhiled and unclean, suffering and abandoned, the four men sat together, waiting for their end to come. It was also a time of famine, so their situation was even more desperate. Then one of them said:

"Why are we sitting here until we die?" (NKJV)

So the four men got up and walked to the nearby camp of the Arameans. When they arrived, they found the camp deserted and they were able to help themselves to fine food, clothes, silver and gold which the soldiers in the camp had left behind. They found treasure. Realising that they should share their find, they went back and shouted over the city wall to the starving Israelites, that the Aramean soldiers had left and there was an abundance of food and treasure. The king sent men to check out the story, then all the people went out and took food, silver, gold and equipment from the camp.

What a fascinating story. The four men could have just accepted their lot, withdrawn from society and given up hope. But despite their illness, they went out and seized the day. They showed courage to face their circumstances and in going out, they found treasure. Not only that, but because of their bravery, they brought food to a starving city full of people and a message of good news to a king.

Perhaps you are going through cancer treatments for the first, second or third time. My heart goes out to you and I pray that God will walk with you and strengthen you every day. I pray that he will hold you and sustain you, that he will care for you and draw close to you. I pray that you too will have the courage to seize the day, to make the most of every opportunity and to live life to the full. This is what Jesus promised:

'I have come that they may have life, and have it to the full.'
John 10 v 10

God doesn't want us to give up. Even in desperate times, there are treasures to be found. God has blessings to give us whatever the circumstances or prognosis. He brings us fulness of life even in our darkest hours. His faithfulness continues despite our disease. His love for us endures throughout our experiences, and he will provide at our time of need. The good news we know and have received is something we need to tell others about. His great provision is not just for us, but for those around us and who come after us - so we need to share it.

As I write this, yesterday was Good Friday and at the quiet afternoon service I attended, our curate, Amanda, gave out nails with a tag on them that said "Love stronger than death." God's love for us, shown through Jesus Christ, is stronger than death. We are totally and utterly loved by God, whether we live or die. Song of Songs talks about the depth and power of love:

'Place me like a seal over your heart,
  like a seal on your arm;
for love is as strong as death,
  its jealousy unyielding as the grave.
It burns like blazing fire,
  like a mighty flame.
Many waters cannot quench love;
  rivers cannot sweep it away.
If one were to give
  all the wealth of one's house for love,
  it would be utterly scorned.'
Song of Songs 8 v 6-7

If our love for one another can be so very strong, then how much greater is God's love for us. In Ephesians, Paul urges us to:

'Grasp how wide and long and high and deep is the love of Christ, and to know this love that surpasses knowledge - that you may be filled to

the measure of all the fulness of God.'
Ephesians 3 v 18-19

Even when we face death, this cannot separate us from God's great love for us - nothing can.

'No, in all these things we are more than conquerors through him
who loved us. For I am convinced that neither death nor life, neither
angels nor demons, neither the present nor the future, nor any powers,
neither height nor depth, nor anything else in all creation, will be able to
separate us from the love of God that is in Christ Jesus our Lord.'
Romans 8 v 37-39

In the Bible, Jesus' friend Lazarus died. His story contains the shortest verse in the Bible: 'Jesus wept' (John 11 v 35). Jesus knows the agony and heartbreak that death causes, the anguish suffered by the loved ones left behind. But Jesus spoke words of comfort, hope and truth to Lazarus' sister Martha, and then as proof that his words were real, he raised Lazarus from the dead.

'Jesus said to her, "I am the resurrection and the life. The one who
believes in me will live, even though they die."'
John 11 v 25

What fantastic words spoken by Jesus. Even when we face death, if we believe in him, we have that same promise of resurrection, because Jesus breathes life and is the giver of eternal life. When one of the robbers crucified next to Jesus asked to be remembered by him in the afterlife, Jesus told him that that very day, he would be with him in paradise (Luke 23 v 43). Death is a gateway into heaven, a step into eternal glory, slipping through a veil into God's presence, so we don't need to be afraid. I remember as a child sitting in our Presbyterian church with my mum and dad and singing the same quiet song at the end of each service. I can't remember any other words than the very last line of the last verse, which said:

'God be at mine end, and at my departing.'

God is with us always - whether we live or die. He never leaves us.

'And surely I am with you always, to the very end of the age.'
Matthew 28 v 20

So seize the day, embrace the present and face the future with courage. Do not be gripped by fear and worry - but pray that your heavenly father will fill you with his strength and courage. Know you are the object of God's absolute love and adoration and that he will be with you always.

How deep the Father's love for us,
How vast beyond all measure
That He should give His only Son
To make a wretch His treasure

How great the pain of searing loss,
The Father turns His face away
As wounds which mar the chosen One,
Bring many sons to glory

Behold the Man upon a cross,
My sin upon His shoulders
Ashamed I hear my mocking voice,
Call out among the scoffers

It was my sin that held Him there
Until it was accomplished
His dying breath has brought me life
I know that it is finished

I will not boast in anything
No gifts, no power, no wisdom
But I will boast in Jesus Christ
His death and resurrection

Why should I gain from His reward?
I cannot give an answer
But this I know with all my heart
His wounds have paid my ransom

Stuart Townend
Copright © 1995 Thankyou Music

Chapter Twenty Three
Amazing Grace

As I look back on this book, it hasn't quite followed the original plan I had intended. I've added bits and taken away bits, included funny bits and sad bits. I've quoted often from the Bible and included songs and words from other people and books. I've rambled on a lot about my own experiences and those of the people around me. I've included my suggestions and ideas. But through all of the chapters, all of the stories and explanations, all of the heartfelt words I have written - is one underlying theme, one constant factor amidst it all: God's amazing grace.

We often use the word 'grace' without it being clearly defined - saying grace at meals, we talk about the grace and elegance of ballet dancers, know ladies called Grace, talk about God's grace to us - but what does the word actually mean? In my old church, the pastor used the acronym G.R.A.C.E. - 'God's Riches At Christ's Expense'. In other words, all that God can possibly give to us, all of his rich provision in our lives, not because we are worthy, but because of Christ's sacrifice. We can't earn God's grace and we don't have to give it back. It is a gift that he pours into our lives.

> *'For it is by grace you have been saved, through faith—and this is not from yourselves, it is the gift of God—not by works, so that no one can boast.'*
> *Ephesians 2 v 8-9*

To me, grace means total and undeserved love. A love that sustains us in our trials. It means unending kindness to the unworthy; overwhelming goodness to the unlovely; overflowing forgiveness to the undeserving. Grace makes the plain things precious; grace transforms the ugly into all that is beautiful. Grace is the humility of the servant king who kneels and washes his disciples' feet. Grace is the awesome creator's hands surrendering to cruel nails on a cross. Grace is walking alongside us in our suffering and telling us we are utterly loved.

One of my favourite psalms, which talks about the meaning of grace, is Psalm eight which says:

> 'When I consider your heavens,
>   the work of your fingers,
> the moon and the stars,
>   which you have set in place,
> what are mere mortals that you are mindful of them,
>   human beings that you care for them?
> You have made them a little lower than the heavenly beings
>   and crowned them with glory and honour.'
> Psalm 8 v 3-5

When I think of the seven billion people on this planet and the sixty million people currently living in my country - it makes me think - who am I that God would know anything about me? Who am I that God would even notice my illness? How can the creator of heaven and earth be bothered to be concerned about me? How can the giver of life be even vaguely interested in me?

Yet the truth is, that incredibly, he is! God who created the universe - who formed the earth, who created animals and creatures, who created planets and stars - he knows me personally, he watches me and he loves me. How amazing! I am nobody special. I am just an ordinary girl, living an ordinary life and facing an increasingly ordinary illness. But God, the amazing and awesome Father, gives me his extra-ordinary love and friendship. God sent his only son, Jesus Christ, to be sacrificed in my place in order that I can know him. God, the creator of life, walks with me and lives in me, sharing every step and breath of my life. How amazing.

I love the song 'Amazing Grace' which talks about how underserving we are of such incredible love:

> Amazing Grace, how sweet the sound,
> That saved a wretch like me
> I once was lost but now am found,
> Was blind, but now, I see.

T'was Grace that taught my heart to fear.
And Grace, my fears relieved.
How precious did that Grace appear
the hour I first believed.

Through many dangers, toils and snares
we have already come.
T'was Grace that brought us safe thus far
and Grace will lead us home.

The Lord has promised good to me
His word my hope secures.
He will my shield and portion be
as long as life endures.

Yea, when this flesh and heart shall fail,
and mortal life shall cease,
I shall possess within the veil,
a life of joy and peace

When we've been there ten thousand years
bright shining as the sun.
We've no less days to sing God's praise
then when we've first begun.

Amazing Grace, how sweet the sound,
That saved a wretch like me
I once was lost but now am found,
Was blind, but now, I see.
John Newton 1779

God's love has indeed carried me safe this far. His grace has strengthened and comforted me, upheld and blessed me. Through the toils and trials, through the dangers and fears, he has held me and sustained me. When I look to the future, I know it will be the same - his grace will carry on. In my life I know his joy and peace, and in my death I will live to praise him for all eternity.

When I look back at this book, I realise I have written a love story. A story about the depth of God's amazing love for me, my awakening realisation of this and my deepening love for him as a natural response. I do feel in many ways that I was blind before and now I see. I was blind to who he was, blind to the way I was living my life, blind to how precious the people are around me, blind to the good news that I need to share more with others. But through this horrible journey, through the months of crying and anguish, my eyes and my heart have been opened, my mind fully focused and I hope and pray that I will never be the same again.

Although I wouldn't go as far as using the word 'good' in this sentence, to some extent, I can agree with the psalmist who said:

> 'It was good for me to be afflicted
>   so that I might learn your decrees.'
> Psalm 119 v 71

In the Message Bible, the same verse is given the following translation:

> 'My troubles turned out all for the best—
>   they forced me to learn from your textbook.
> Truth from your mouth means more to me
>   than striking it rich in a gold mine.'

In some ways I can accept that this illness was God's plan for me, because it has drawn me much closer to my heavenly father and taught me more about the reality of his ways and his grace.

I recently attended a church service where I was asked to give my testimony and talk about God's grace. Another lady who was speaking, talked about grace meaning 'God's enoughness'. She quoted the brilliant verse from 2 Corinthians 12 v 9-10:

> '[The Lord] said to me,"My grace is sufficient for you, for my power is made perfect in weakness." Therefore I will boast all the more gladly about my weaknesses, so that Christ's power may rest on me. That is why, for Christ's sake, I delight in weaknesses, in insults, in hardships, in persecutions, in difficulties. For when I am weak, then I am strong.'

I love the part that says 'my grace is sufficient for you'. God gives us what we need as we walk through both good and difficult times in our lives. He is our sufficiency; he is enough. Each day as I have walked along this journey, God has given me just enough strength, just enough peace, just enough perseverence and just enough hope for each day - just enough to keep me going. My mum used to have a plate on her wall that said 'Keep me going, Lord' - and that is just what he did.

There is a story in the Bible (Exodus 16) where the Israelites wandered in the desert for forty years and each day, God sent a bread called 'manna' for the Israelites to eat. He promised to send just enough every day- bread that was fresh and filling, every day. If the Israelites tried to take too much, by the next day it was rotten and had to be thrown away. God's grace is like that manna. He pours down just what we need in every situation. We often want more - more peace, more strength, more courage - but God himself knows the exact quantities we need each day. We don't need to keep hold of today's blessings, because we have the assurance that tomorrow God's grace will pour down all that we need for a new day. That is his promise to us - to feed and sustain us, because of his great love for us - every day.

When I was thinking about what to say in my testimony in the church, it dawned on me that my key verse - 1 Peter 5 v 10 - which had been my anchor through the storm, referred to God as 'the God of all grace.' He is not a God of a little bit of grace - a little bit of kindness and compassion, but instead he is absolutley full of grace. He is absolutley overflowing with love for us and provision for our lives. He delights to fill us with himself and give us all that we need in every circumstance.

Another amazing thing about grace is that we can always approach God and ask for it. It is freely available to us at any time. The Bible says that we have an open invitation to seek more grace in our lives:

> *'Let us then approach the throne of grace with confidence, so that we may receive mercy and find grace to help us in our time of need.'*
> *Hebrews 4 v 16*

So I pray that as you live your life, as you face every trial and every situation, you may know God's grace in a new and deeper way. I pray that you too, would know his adequate provision for your life - his overflowing love and kindness for you - freely and undeservedly available to you, and his 'enoughness' for your every need.

> *'Grace and peace to you from God our Father and from the Lord Jesus Christ.'*
> *Romans 1 v 7*

And may the grace of our Lord Jesus Christ, the love of God and the fellowship of the Holy Spirit, be with you, today and always. Amen.

Chapter Twenty Four
With You

I remember when the boys were younger, if they weren't very keen on their dinner, I would cajole them into eating it with the words 'just one more.' Often being the really cruel mother that I am, I'd then say it again and force another mouthful of broccoli and mash into their protesting mouths as they said, 'You said that before!' I'd reply with 'Well this time I mean it!' Poor children!

It's a bit like that with this chapter. I had planned that my chapter on grace would be the last one, but there are still a few morsels I would like to feed you, before we finish this book together.

I am so struck by God's tangible presence with me as I have walked through this experience of ill health and suffering. I have already referred to this experience like a storm in my life. But the incredible reality that God has spoken to me and Ian, again and again, is 'I am with you!'

We were so blessed recently to go to Disney and Universal Studios in Orlando and we had a fantastic time together, as a celebration of my recovery. One of the attractions in Universal Studios was called 'Twister' and was a film studio recreation of a tornado. It was absolutley gripping. We stood huddled together in the street, covered in darkness, with fire roaring in front of us, trees falling over around us, cars and even cows flying through the air, and water soaking us, as the tornado came close. It was breathtaking! I've always loved the film 'The Wizard of Oz' and the part where Dorothy's house gets taken up in the tornado and she sees cows and houses, bikes and belongings flying through the air. What strikes me about both of these scenes is that despite all of the destruction that is caused, all of the upheaval, fear and turmoil, despite roots being torn and lives being ripped apart, there is peace and stillness in the central eye of the storm.

God's promise is not to save us from storms - not to keep us from bad things happening in our lives - but that in the heart of it, in the middle of the crisis - he promises that will be with us.

I love the story in the Bible in Daniel chapter three with Meshach, Shadrach and Abednego (such brilliant names!). These three men were followers of God and decided not to obey the king's orders to worship a gold idol the king had created, even though they knew this would cost them their lives. Their words show true courage:

> *'We do not need to defend ourselves before you in this matter. If we are thrown in the blazing furnance, the God we serve is able to save us from it and he will rescue us from your hand. But even if he does not, we want you to know, O king, that we will not serve your gods or worship the image of gold you have set up.'*
> *Daniel 3 v 16-17*

Needless to say, the men were then thrown into the fire for disobeying the king's orders.The king was so furious that he ordered that the fire be heated seven times hotter than usual and the soldiers that threw the men into the fire, actually died because it was so hot. But here is the strange thing. When the king looked into the furnace, he could not believe his eyes, because there was someone else in the fire too.

> *'Then King Nebuchadnezzar leaped to his feet in amazement and asked his advisers, "Weren't there three men that we tied up and threw into the fire?"*
> *They replied, "Certainly, Your Majesty."*
> *He said, "Look! I see four men walking around in the fire, unbound and unharmed, and the fourth looks like a son of the gods."'*
> *Daniel 3 v 24-25*

I was shocked when I heard a sermon a few years ago about this passage and the pastor talked about that fourth person being Jesus. I had honestly never considered that that could be Jesus in the fire with the men, as this is an Old Testament story. From the king's words, this was obviously a supernatural person in the fire with the men. It could have been an angel, but I believe it was almost certainly Jesus with them.

Similarly a few chapters on, Daniel, another faithful follower of the Lord, had a similar encounter when he chose to continue praying to God and not to King Darius. As a result he ended up being thrown into the lions' den. This king actually regretted authorising this law and was anxious to see if Daniel's God was real and if he would save him.

> *'At the first light of dawn, the king got up and hurried to the lions' den.*
> *When he came near the den, he called to Daniel in an anguished voice,*
> *"Daniel, servant of the living God, has your God, whom you serve*
> *continually, been able to rescue you from the lions?"*
> *Daniel answered, "May the king live forever! My God sent his angel,*
> *and he shut the mouths of the lions. They have not hurt me, because I*
> *was found innocent in his sight."'*
> *Daniel 6 v 19-21*

Our lives on earth are full of fires and lions - of situations that can burn us, consume and destroy us. But the good news, in fact the incredible news, is that God is WITH US! He is there in the heart of the storm; in the den of the lions - protecting us and closing the mouths of all that tries to rip us apart; he is walking around with us, in the blazing and scorching fire. We don't need to be afraid. We don't need to run away. We can face every circumstance and every difficulty because he is with us.

I often feel like Peter in Matthew chapter 14. Here the disciples were together in a boat out on a lake, when wild winds began to blow. Jesus appeared and started walking on the water. The disciples were all terrified but Peter got out of the boat and he too started walking on water, towards Jesus. However, as he looked around him at the waves, the wind and the darkness, he began to sink.

> *'But when he saw the wind, he was afraid and, beginning to sink, cried*
> *out "Lord save me!" Immediately Jesus reached out his hand and*
> *caught him.'*
> *Matthew 14 v 29-30*

It is so easy for us to look at the waves and the winds - to focus on the circumstances and the storm of emotions that rise up in response. It is so easy to start to sink in life, when we go through difficult times - be that cancer or any other hardship. It is so easy to forget that God is with us. He never leaves us or forgets about us. Jesus himself is right there next to us - in the heart of the storm, out on the lake, in the midst of the darkness and that when we cry out to him, he reaches out and catches us too.

Chapter Twenty Five
A Commission of Grace

A little like that extra spoonful being given to my children - this really is the last chapter!

As you have read this book and the story of my cancer experience, I hope that you have found strength, peace and encouragement for your soul. If you are going through breast cancer or any other cancer treatment yourself, my heart goes out to you and I pray that you too will know God's grace in your life – his provision and strength, just enough for each and every day. I hope that just as God has ministered and spoken words to me, that by me sharing these words with you, he would encourage and uplift you also. We don't know all the answers to life's questions - such as why cancer happens. But I hope that you may have found some comfort in the fact that God knows the answers when we don't, and that he cares deeply for each one of us.

Maybe you are the friend or family member of a person with cancer, or maybe you are going through different trials and suffering. Whatever your situation, I hope and pray that God will have spoken words of love and strength into your heart, as you have read these pages.

I pray that as you go through your sad times - times of darkness and tears, times of anguish and questioning, times of passing through the storm and the fire - that you too would know that God is indeed with you. That he walks right alongside you; a father bursting with love and adoration for you, his precious child; attentively watching over you and holding your right hand.

I hope that the comfort I have received from God has reached out to you from these very pages and that the words in Corinthians I have already quoted, have become a reality:

> *'Praise be to the God and Father of our Lord Jesus Christ, the Father of compassion and the God of all comfort, who comforts us in all our troubles, so that we can comfort those in any trouble with the comfort we ourselves receive from God.'*
> *2 Corinthians 1 v 3-4*

I hope that the Lord himself has encouraged you as you have read this book:

'May our Lord Jesus Christ himself and God our Father, who loved
us and by his grace gave us eternal encouragement and good hope,
encourage your hearts and strengthen you in every good deed and word.'
2 Thessalonians 2 v 16-17

God is worthy to be praised in all walks of life, in all situations and even amongst our suffering, when it hurts most. My husband Ian's favourite song is 'Blessed be your Name' and the words that talk about pain in the offering, are particularly poignant:

Blessed Be Your name
In the land that is plentiful
Where Your streams of abundance flow
Blessed be Your name

Blessed Be Your name
When I'm found in the desert place
Though I walk through the wilderness
Blessed Be Your name

Every blessing You pour out
I'll turn back to praise
When the darkness closes in, Lord
Still I will say

Blessed be the name of the Lord
Blessed be Your name
Blessed be the name of the Lord
Blessed be Your glorious name

Blessed be Your name
When the sun's shining down on me
When the world's 'all as it should be'
Blessed be Your name

Blessed be Your name
On the road marked with suffering
Though there's pain in the offering
Blessed be Your name

Every blessing You pour out
I'll turn back to praise
When the darkness closes in, Lord
Still I will say

Blessed be the name of the Lord
Blessed be Your name
Blessed be the name of the Lord
Blessed be Your glorious name

Blessed be the name of the Lord
Blessed be Your name
Blessed be the name of the Lord
Blessed be Your glorious name

You give and take away
You give and take away
My heart will choose to say
Lord, blessed be Your name

Beth Redman, Matt Redman
Copyright © 2002 Thankyou Music*

I sincerely do praise God and thank him for his faithfulness to me throughout this episode in my life. I do truly worship his name for all that he has blessed me with, for who he is and for all that he has given to me.

I feel so grateful for God's grace in this situation and in my life, but what I feel him saying to me is that this grace is not just for me - it's for me to share. His kindness and compassion are not just for me to remember, but for me to give away. His strength and provision are not just for me to be grateful for, but for me to pass onto others. It is his commission of grace.

As I write this, I am soon to be leaving my job in the NHS as Ian begins his training to become a vicar in the Church of England. I feel excited (and nervous at the same time!) not only about what God has got in store for Ian, but for me too. I have such a desire within me now to find others who are going through the experience of cancer and to support and share with them all that God has given to me. I'm hoping very much to link up with hospital chaplains in Bristol, where we will be living, to visit people with cancer and pray with and for them, as they receive their treatment. My heart's focus has shifted from teaching deaf people to speak, to teaching sick people to hear. To hear that still small voice and a message of love amidst suffering, of strength amidst heartbreak, of God's unique friendship amidst the loneliness.

Maybe you too have known God's strength in your circumstances and inexplicable peace as you have passed through a crisis. Maybe you too have been touched by his grace and equipped in your journey. In the same way - you too have a commission of grace. You too need to share that grace with those around you. You too need to pass on the comfort you have received and tell others of the great love you have known in the Father's arms. Grace is not just something for the church, it is God's gift to the whole world. Jesus sends us out to share his love with those around us. We need to live a life that is full of him and that overflows with his love, grace and compassion, to the people who share our lives:

'Again Jesus said, "Peace be with you! As the Father has sent me, I am sending you."' John 20 v 21

'Walk in the way of love, just as Christ loved us' Ephesians 1 v 5

Perhaps you have never really thought much about God before. You may or may not have believed in him, and never been sure about how relevant he is in today's modern world. Thank you for reading this book. I hope that it has challenged you and made you think. I hope that it has generated questions and searching in your own heart, and made you thirsty to find out more about God.

Whatever your situation or circumstance, Jesus calls all those who are hungry, thirsty, broken and weary.

'Then Jesus declared, "I am the bread of life. Whoever comes to me

will never go hungry, and whoever believes in me will never be thirsty.'
John 6 v 35

'Come to me, all you who are weary and burdened, and I will give
you rest. Take my yoke upon you and learn from me, for I am
gentle and humble in heart, and you will find rest for your souls.'
Matthew 11 v 28-29

So go in peace, live each day knowing that your life is an occasion - a gift from God. May God heal you from past wounds and heartbreak. May he bring you all strength and comfort through the power of his Holy Spirit. In your present, may he fill you with his rest. In your future, may you have courage, knowing that your heavenly father already knows all that lies ahead, and he has a plan for you. Share God's amazing grace with those around you. May you have a song to sing, a story to tell and the courage to share it.

Men of faith rise up and sing
Of the great and glorious King
You are strong when you feel weak
In your brokeness complete

Shout to the North and the South
Sing to the East and the West
Jesus is saviour to all
Lord of heaven and earth

Rise up women of the truth
Stand and sing to broken hearts
Who can know the healing power
Of our awesome King of love

We've been through fire we've been
through rain
We've been refined by the power of his name
We've fallen deeper in love with you
You've burned the truth on our lips

Rise up church with broken wings
Fill this place with songs again
Of our God who reigns on high
By his grace again we'll fly

May God bless you mightily, so that you can bless others. May he strengthen and comfort you, so that you can serve others. May he shine his light on you, so that you can reflect him in every situation. May your right hand be firmly in his, today and always.

'The LORD bless you
and keep you;
the LORD make his face shine on you
and be gracious to you;
the LORD turn his face toward you
and give you peace.'
Numbers 6 v 24-26

'Now may the Lord of peace himself give you peace at all times and in every way. The Lord be with all of you.'
2 Thessalonians 3 v 16

And may you always remember the eternal promise of your loving, heavenly Father:

'I am the LORD your God
who takes hold of your right hand
and says to you, Do not fear;
I will help you.'
Isaiah 41 v 13

Amen.

APPENDICES

Appendix 1 - How and When to Check your Breasts
Appendix 2 - Useful Websites
Appendix 3 - Postscript
Appendix 4 - References

APPENDIX ONE - HOW AND WHEN TO CHECK YOUR BREASTS

This appendix contains an amalgamation of information from a number of sources including - 'Your breasts, your health: a quick guide to being breast aware' - by Breast Cancer Care; 'Breast Awareness' by WNCC Cancer Aware (Women's Nationwide Cancer Control Campaign); information from 'This Morning' by Dr Chris Steele (6.10.10), and discussion with my own GP.

The Importance of Checking

'Breast cancer is the most common cancer in the UK' (Breast Cancer Care leaflet). Statistics indicate that a woman's risk of breast cancer increases with age and as such, in the UK, only ladies of 50 or older are currently screened. This is due to reduce to 47 years of age, but there are no plans to screen younger women. However, 20% of breast cancer occurs in women under 50, for whom there is no screening. This means that a fifth of all breast cancer diagnoses, need to be detected and initiated by women themselves. Earlier detection and intervention, means better rates of survival.

Who should check?

All ladies should start to check their breasts from their early twenties. Older ladies who are screened, should also check themselves because cancer may start between mammograms. Although much less common, breast cancer does occur in men and so men should also check themselves.

When should you check?

Some sources recommend checking every week, but this may be too frequent. My GP recommended checking once per month, exactly a week after your period has started. Breasts become harder and naturally lumpy before a woman has her monthly period, so it is important to check your breasts when your period has finished. After the menopause, breasts usually become softer and less lumpy and women should continue to check themselves on a monthly basis.

What do you need?
- Your eyes
- A mirror
- Your hands
- The memory to check
- The courage to go for investigations, if you need to

What do you do?
You need to get to know what is normal for you, in order to spot anything that is not normal. Breasts are often naturally lumpy and you will get used to how your breasts look and feel, the more often you check.

1. Look first:
Get used to the physical appearance of your breasts. Look at their shape and size, and the position of your nipples. Look facing the mirror and from the side. Look with your arms by your sides, your arms up in the air and your hands on your hips. Look standing up straight and look leaning forward.

Look for:
- Anything that is new for you
- Any changes in shape or size of your breasts
- Any change in skin texture - such as dimpling/puckering
- Any visible lumps or thickening
- Redness or a rash on the skin or nipple
- Any fluid/blood leaking from the nipple when you are not pregnant or breast feeding
- Your nipple being pulled in (inverted) or any changes in shape or position (e.g. pointing to the side)
- A swelling in your armpit or around your collarbone
- Veins that stand out more than usual
- Constant pain in your breast or armpit (not just premenstrual and menstrual breast pain).

2. Feel second:

You can feel your breasts in the bath or shower or when getting changed - whenever suits you. Ladies with larger breasts may be better lying down. Use your right hand to check your left breast and left hand to check your right breast. Use the pads of your fingers, not the finger tips. Keep your fingers together and flat. Press gently but firmly. Use circular movements going round your breast, in ever increasing circles. Check the whole breast including under your armpits and up to your collarbone/base of your neck. Then use the flat of your hand to press down with big circular movements on the whole of your breast. Squeeze your nipple to check for any discharge. Repeat on the other side.

Feel for:

- Anything that is new for you
- A lump or thickening that feels different from the rest of the breast tissue
- A lump that is not normal for you
- A lump that is specific to one breast

What should you do if you notice a lump or any of the above?

Be brave and visit your GP straight away. Don't ignore anything you may have found. Most changes in breasts are not due to breast cancer, but it is always worth being checked. Your GP may refer you for a mammogram, ultrasound scan or a biopsy. Some of these are not pleasant and tests may cause you worry - but always remember that earlier detection means treatment is often more effective. Hopefully it will turn out to be something other than cancer, but it is not worth the risk of ignoring anything that concerns you. Your life and your family are worth protecting!

What can you do to reduce your risk of breast cancer?

It is not clear what exactly causes breast cancer for most people, but risks can be reduced by living a healthy lifestyle. This includes:

- Eating a good diet with lots of fruit and vegetables
- Cutting down on sugar, salt and fatty foods
- Losing weight and maintaining a healthy weight
- Keeping fit and taking part in regular exercise

- Reducing how much alcohol you drink
- Checking your breasts regularly
- Taking up the offer of regular screening if you are over 50

So be brave. Check yourself regularly. Watch out for changes and see your doctor if you have any concerns. Earlier diagnosis means more effective treatment and better survival rates. Remember you are worth it! It could save your life. It saved mine.

APPENDIX TWO - USEFUL WEBSITES

www.breastcancercare.org.uk A wealth of information and support packages for women diagnosed with breast cancer. Online support groups and forums, a free helpline, newsblogs including up to date research, younger women's forums. Also breast cancer care produce an excellent DVD called 'Eating Well, being active: Healthy Living after breast cancer.' (Order free from the website).

www.macmillan.org.uk Macmillan and 'Cancerbackup' merged in 2008. Together, they provide an excellent source of information on all aspects of cancer. Cancerbackup produce lots of leaflets – such as 'how to talk to your children about cancer', and 'coping with hair loss'. Advice for people living with cancer and their families.

www.breastcancer.org Comprehensive information on all things to do with breast cancer including side effects, working lives and reducing risk.

www.cancerresearchuk.org Up to date research and treatment developments. Personal stories and patient information.

www.cancer.net Informative American website. Useful information on healthy living after cancer.

www.amoena.com A website aimed at improving women's quality of life after breast surgery and breast cancer. A wide range of products to buy, aimed at restoring a positive body image. See also the 'Amoena life online' section - linked to the

Amoena life magazine. Lots of information, medical updates and support.

www.wnccc.org.uk (Women's Nationwide Cancer Control Campaign). Information about breast awareness.

www.lymphoedema.org The Lymphoedema Support Network is a UK charity offering advice and support to all people who develop lymphoedema.

http://www.webmd.com/breast-cancer/guide/side-effects-lymphedema This webpage is full of information about lymphoedema - what causes it, how to deal with it, how to avoid it etc - all very useful.

www.biblegateway.com Find any verse or passage of the Bible in many translations.

www.nanciegoudie.com and **www.ngm.org.uk** Find out about Nancy Goudie's spiritual health weekends, mentioned in chapter 17. Also visit the website to purchase books and CDs, including 'You are Special'.

www.slimmingworld.com Find a local group. Online support and recipes, plus an excellent magazine.

Appendix Three
Postscript

Since writing 'My Right Hand in the Father's', I have moved with my family to Bristol, where Ian is currently studying at Trinity Theological College to be ordained in the Church of England. When I became well again, there was a definite part of me that wanted to forget this horrible season in my life. I also felt afraid that if I followed the calling that God was putting on my life, to help support people with cancer, that I would live in fear of its return and be faced with too many painful memories.

What I felt the Lord say to me, was that for me to forget - is to forget the story of his grace. To forget this time, is to forget his care and faithfulness to me. I need to remember and hold on to that commission of grace. God has also done an amazing work releasing me from a lot of fear of cancer, through a Beth Moore Bible Study (Breaking Free), which I would highly recommend. Although I do still worry and feel afraid at times, I know 'My times are in his hands' (Psalm 31 v 15) and 'God has ordained every day of my life' (Psalm 139 v 16).

God has therefore continued to stir in me a desire to reach out to people affected by cancer, and to pass on to them the strength and comfort he gave to me. I was shocked to learn that there is no Christian cancer support charity in the UK that I can find. As I have researched and prayed, God has given me a vision for 'Firm Roots Cancer Support', which is just setting up in Bristol at the time of going to press. My belief is that if your roots are in Christ, you will stand in the storm.

The aim of the ministry is to pray with and for people affected by cancer and my church, St Matthew's, Kingsdown, has just started a monthly Cancer Prayer Support Group. There are plans to set up a prayer network with local churches in Bristol, to pray for people and families affected by cancer, as well as to offer one day and weekend retreats and hospital visiting. The ministry is also aiming to offer practical support such as meal delivery, ironing, transport to appointments, spouse support and generally walking alongside people affected

by a diagnosis. What an opportunity we have to 'bind up the brokenhearted...
to comfort all who mourn... and bestow on them a crown of beauty instead of
ashes' (Isaiah 61). That is my desire. I feel completely inadequate to start this
work, but I know I just need to walk in obedience and remember that I have a
great big God, in whom all things are possible.

'The one who calls you is faithful and he will do it' (1 Thessalonians 5 v 24).

To God be all the glory!

With much love in Christ,

Helen Jones
June 2012

Appendix Four
References

1. Scripture quotations taken from the HOLY BIBLE, NEW INTERNATIONAL VERSION. Copyright © 1973, 1978, 1984 by International Bible Society. Used by permission.
2. P. 17 'The Word for Today; Encouraging words every day' by Bob and Debby Gass. Produced by UCB – United Christian Broadcasting, UCB Operations Centre, Westport Road, Stoke on Trent, UK ST6 4JF. Email: ucb@ucb.co.uk. Contact UCB directly for free copies of 'The Word for Today'. Quote used with permission.
3. P.22 'I do not know what lies ahead.' Smith Alfred/Clarke Eugene. © 1958 New Spring Publishing/Imagem/Small Stone Media BV, Holland (Admin. by Song Solutions Daybreak (www.songsolutions.org). Used with permission.
4. P.29 'I will sing the wondrous story.' Rowley (words)/ PD Prichard. © 1937 Harper Collins Religious (Admin. by Song Solutions Copycare www.songsolutions.org). Used with permission.
5. P.33 'Fear Not – For I am with you always.' Promise Book by Max Lucado. Thomas Nelson Inc.
6. P. 46 'The Word for Today.' 3rd June 2010. Used with permission.
7. P47 Even though I walk, You never let go.' Beth Redman & Matt Redman Copyright © 2005 Thankyou Music. Used with permission.
8. P.54 'My life is but a Weaving.' A poem by Benjamin Malachi Franklin 1882-1965.
9. P. 59 'The Shack' by William Young, Hodder & Stoughton, 2008.
10. P 65 'Make me a channel of your peace' by Sebastian Temple. Dedicated to Mrs. Frances Tracy. © 1967, OCP, 5536 NE Hassalo, Portland OR 97213. All rights reserved. Used with permission.
11. P. 72 'Prayer Shawls' – a prayer by Janet Bristow www.shawlministry.com/prayers.htm
12. P. 77 'The Word for Today', UCB. 8th August 2010. Used with permission.
13. P.78 'His banner over me.' Prosch Kevin. © Mercy/Vineyard Publishing (Admin. by Song Solutions Copycare www.songsolutions.org). Use with permission.

14. P.79 'Men are from Mars, Women are from Venus' by John Gray. Harper Element Publishers 2002.
15. P.80 'Life Application Study Bible' p. 1149. Copyright [1991] David C Cook. Life Application Study Bible (NIV) notes only. Publisher permission required to reproduce. All rights reserved.
16. P. 93 'You are Special' by Nancy Goudie (p.57). Published by NGM New Generation Music 2011. Used with permission.
17. P. 96 'Special One' by Ray Goudie and Phil Barlow, NGM 2011. Used with permission.
18. P. 102 'Time to Jump' by Ian Jones, 2003.
19. P.106 Quote attributed to St Francis of Assissi – 'Chapter XVII of his Rule of 1221.'
20. P.111 'Names and titles of God' by Dr R. F. Wilson. Copyright Ralph F. Wilson. <pastorjoyfulheart.com>. All rights reserved. Used by permission.
21. P.118 'Amoena Life Magazine' Issue 29. Www.amoena.com Amoena 1701 Barrett Lakes Boulevard, Suite 410, Kennesaw, GA 30144, USA.
22. P. 123 Scriptures (marked GNB) are taken from the Good News Bible published by The Bible Societies/Collins © American Bible Society.
23. P. 129 'Be Thou my Vision' by Mary Byrne 1905. The Random House Group Ltd.
24. P. 131 'Holy Bible: New King James Version' Nelson Publishers, 1993.
25. P. 134 'How deep the Father's love for us' by Stuart Townend. Copyright © 1995 Thankyou Music
26. P. 137 'Amazing Grace' by John Newton, 1779. Copyright Roland Fudge.
27. P. 139 'The Message Bible; the Bible in Contemporary Language' by Eugene H Peterson. Nav Press www.navpress.com
28. P. 146 'Blessed be your Name' by Beth & Matt Redman. Copyright © 2002 Thankyou Music
29. P. 149 'Men of Faith Shout to the North' by Martin Smith Copyright © 1995 Curious? Music/Kingswaysongs
30. Appendix Three – 'Breaking Free' Bible Study & DVD series by Beth Moore. LifeWay Press, Nashville, Tennessee, USA. Living Proof Ministries www.lproof.org and www.lifeway.com